BIRD WATCHER'S
Life List & Diary

BERNARD A. FASHINGBAUER

PHIL MISSELDINE
_____
NAME

_____
ADDRESS

_____
CITY / STATE / ZIP

_____
PHONE

_____
DATE BEGUN

Culpepper Press Minneapolis

INTRODUCTION

Bird-watching is now Number One! With the possible exception of combined hunting and fishing sports, this absorbing pastime ranks first among worldwide hobbies, even surpassing stamp and coin collecting as the choice of millions.

Bird-watching as a hobby begins simply enough. You seek out birds, the more species the better, and repeated observations of the same species are not considered boring. Like many hobbies, it can be enhanced by travel and, better than most, it can be enjoyed almost any place on earth—usually at little or no additional cost. Furthermore, bird-watching can be enjoyed twenty-four hours a day any season of the year throughout much of the world, and it lends itself to both solo or group outings. It can be a pleasing, casual episode in the lives of many and may approach or even exceed fanaticism with more than a few. Thousands of observers limit their viewing to through the window and perhaps backyard feeding stations, whereas at the other extreme, growing numbers participate (usually for charitable fund-raising causes) in grueling long-distance "birding" marathons.

Birds, more so than other groups of animals, offer beauty and charm in the form of color, song, and fascinating behavioral traits. A few species can become a nuisance, but generally birds endear themselves to people of all ages. To experience the joy of this hobby, begin with this Bird Watcher's Life List and Diary. Record the various species that you discover around your home in the city or in the country, at local and national parks, on business and leisure travels—wherever you encounter birds!

Those whose avocational or professional training has already inspired systematic note-taking will require no prompting regarding the value of proper

Bird Watcher's Life List & Diary
Copyright © 1989 Culpepper Press, Inc.

ISBN 0-929636-03-1   10 9 8 7 6 5 4 3 2 1

CULPEPPER PRESS
2901 Fourth St. SE
Minneapolis, MN 55414

record-keeping. But I urge more casual novices to record their field notes carefully and thoroughly so that they may contribute to a fund of scientific knowledge. Information of this kind, when reliably gathered, becomes increasingly valuable in assessing the environmental quality of our nation and other regions of the world.

To make checklist records scientifically useful and to sustain your personal interest, consider entering the following types of information under each species' name: names of your companions; altitude in mountainous terrain; observed bird behavior such as calling, singing, flying, swimming, feeding, territorial defense, courtship and nest building; relative abundance; weather conditions; and whatever else you find personally fulfilling. As years pass, what you had regarded as commonplace may become history, and you will have helped write it! But perhaps of equal import, you will have experienced pleasant camaraderie likely to greatly enhance the remainder of your life.

Your Life List is almost certain to inspire you to seek greater birding and associated outdoor adventures. Soon you will want to accumulate a nature library, include photography in your outings and "stop and smell the flowers" as you creep up on a particularly unusual bird whose identity puzzles you. Birding is perhaps as close as you can come to a no-lose situation.

Tabulating birds observed is a "big thing" in the lives of many birders, and there are established lists for almost every conceivable occurrence or event. Included are tallies pertaining to backyard observations and other specific areas; counts extending over the period of a day, season or year; special events such as the national annual Christmas Bird Count; breeding bird census; first arrival

CONTENTS

dates in the spring; latest departure dates in the fall. Recently birding marathons have grown rapidly in popularity. For serious birders, the expression "Any excuse for a party" is parlayed into "Any excuse for a bird count."

To most birders the epitome of bird tallies is the Life List. The lengths to which some zealous birders will go to build their life lists merits the attention of even the international media. On a worldwide basis, the long sought numerical goal is the magic 7,000! Of some 8,600 to 9,000 species of birds believed to exist throughout the world, the greatest number recorded seen by any one person is reportedly 6,600. A select few birders are known to have reached 6,000 or more and are striving to exceed this extraordinary achievement. Relatively large sums of time and money have been spent in these intensive endeavors.

A more modest, but nonetheless exceptionally challenging, goal is the search for bird species to be found within North America north of Mexico. This region includes off-shore islands and adjoining ocean areas generally limited to within 100 miles from the mainland. Approximately 850 species are known to occur here. An exact number is difficult to establish as official recognition of North American species, as with other regions of the world, remains in a state of flux. By 1985, according to the American Birding Association (ABA), 439 birders had attained a listing of 600 or more species for this portion of North America. By 1986 one gentleman reached a lifetime listing of 760 North American birds! He headed an exclusive fraternity of less than 50 known members who reached or exceeded the astounding number of 700 species. These accomplishments are certain to increase with time.

Of course the tropical regions of the world host the majority of the known bird species, and the New World is exceptional in this regard. Over 1,600 species are found within several South American countries, and Mexico lists over 1,000. The species that stray over our common border with Mexico add much to the excitement of birding in the southwestern portions of the United States. West Indian species are occasionally discovered in and about Florida, and in the coastal areas of Alaska certain Asian species occur, albeit rarely.

SPECIES INCLUDED IN THIS CHECKLIST

Determining which species of birds to include in this checklist was complicated by indecisions involving several factors. The presence of erratic wanderers from Europe, Asia, Mexico and the Caribbean; intentionally introduced or escaped exotics; and far-ranging pelagic seabirds contributed to the confusion. Many of these "accidentals" are seen only rarely by a minute number of birders, but since they do occur, they invite inclusion in North America's list of avian species. The listing of a few birds in some checklists is based upon as little as a single sighting or two over a period of many years. The merit of including all of these over a region as vast as the northern portion of the North American continent remains questionable and is not easily resolved.

The two major North American checklists, A.O.U. (American Ornithologists Union) and ABA (American Birding Association), served as the basis for this checklist. The decision whether to include a certain introduced species or erratic migrant was tempered slightly with the recognition it was accorded by current avian journals and other ornithological literature. Final inclusion problems were resolved by favoring those erratic species described and/or illustrated in the more recent bird guides, as these form the basis of identification used by birders throughout North America.

The U.S./Mexico border was selected as the southern limit of geographic coverage chiefly for practical reasons, as the inclusion of Mexican and Central American species would have more than doubled the number of entries. Most of North America's tropical birds are customarily treated in separate field guides and checklists—and, following custom, this book does not include them.

CHECKLIST ORDER

The sequential arrangement of the species in this Life List is based upon the most recent (sixth) edition of the A.O.U. checklist published in 1983. This authoritative listing considers the presumed phylogenetic or ancestral relationships among birds ranging from the most primitive to the most advanced. Periodic revisions of this sequence are made only after serious scientific study and contemplation. Resulting taxonomic changes occur as a result of both the "splitting" and "lumping" of bird species. However, such revisions are aggravating to many birders, and name deletions and changes, particularly, are met with some resistance. Fortunately, changes in the name more significantly affect the common or English name of a bird, and the Latin or scientific name remains a stable base for reference when changes occur in the vernacular nomenclature.

FIELD GUIDES AND ASSOCIATED IDENTIFICATION AIDS

Field guides are essential to the proper identification of birds and therefore of tremendous assistance in completing your Life List. An excellent assortment is available for even many of the more remote areas of the world, and field guides are especially thorough in the identification of North American birds. Some guides contain range maps which are of particular assistance to the amateur birder by eliminating from consideration species that occur rarely, if ever, within a specific region being studied.

Of course bird books of all kinds, including the large format monographs, regional studies and several periodic journals and magazines, are also useful

North America, north of Mexico

to the birder. In addition, the many local checklists and both audio and video recordings will significantly assist in identifying many of the more common birds. Learning to identify birds by their songs and calls requires considerable practice, but it is a very effective means of discovery, particularly in heavy cover.

"How To" and "Where To" books referring to bird watching can help the novice become a learned birder. Many tips and ideas set forth in these books are the result of countless hours spent by advanced birders doing exactly what the beginner must learn to become truly proficient in this hobby. Finally, becoming a member of a local bird club and perhaps a national society devoted to bird study will provide much current information and further your enjoyment appreciably.

INTEGRATION OF LIFE LIST AND FIELD GUIDES

To more effectively correlate the use of selected field guides with this Life List, an innovative scheme was devised. In this Life List, for each species we list page references to illustrations and/or descriptions of the species given in three of the most popular field guides to North American birds. The three guides are indicated as G (published by Golden Press), NG (published by National Geographic) and P (authored by Peterson). When making Life List entries, birders can verify their observations about species and also expand their general knowledge of the birds.

Since revised editions frequently alter the sequential numbering of a book's pages, it is necessary to properly identify the field guides chosen. Editions and publication dates are as follows:

G = *A Guide to Field Identification of North American Birds.* Expanded, Revised Edition. Chandler S. Robbins, Bertel Bruun, and Herbert S. Zim. New York: Golden Press, 1983.

NG = *Field Guide to the Birds of North America.* Second Edition. Various authors. Shirley L. Scott, Editor. Washington, D.C.: National Geographic Society, 1987.

P = *A Field Guide to the Birds — East of the Rockies.* Fourth Edition, completely revised and enlarged. Roger Tory Peterson. Boston: Houghton Mifflin Co., 1980. Note: The companion to this eastern & central regional guide is *A Field Guide to Western Birds*, second edition, which although completely revised and enlarged (1969), remains taxonomically out-of-date. In addition there is considerable overlap in the regional coverages provided by the two volumes, resulting in much species duplication. For these reason, I do not include page references to Peterson's western guide in this Life List and Diary.

The number of species listed in these three guides differs significantly; some birds are frequently included in one guide, but not in all. Instances in which a species is not described in a particular guide are indicated by a dash (−). Field guides generally do not include exceptionally erratic migrants and rare introduced species. Hence, some of the birds listed in this publication are not found in any of the three guides; and the birder must look elsewhere for information regarding these "accidental" species.

As new editions are published, birders may wish to keep the guide page number current by adding the proper page references into the Life List.

GOOD BIRDING!

Throughout all your days afield, conduct yourself properly. Don't allow your enthusiasm to cause you to disregard the privacy and quiet of others. Be courteous to everyone, including fellow birders. Birding "ethics" are crucial to a continuation of the usual warm welcome bird watchers are offered worldwide.

Orders:

List of North American Birds

North of Mexico

A.O.U.
Check-list,
Sixth Edition

(Species index on page 213)

Gaviiformes

Podicipediformes

Procellariiformes

Pelecaniformes

Ciconiiformes

Phoenicopteriformes

Anseriformes

Falconiformes

Galliformes

Gruiformes

Charadriiformes

Columbiformes

Psittaciformes

Cuculiformes

Strigiformes

Caprimulgiformes

Apodiformes

Trogoniformes

Coraciiformes

Piciformes

Passeriformes

Loons *(Gaviidae)*

Red-throated Loon   *Gavia stellata*

DATE   **G**18   **NG**20   **P**32

LOCALITY

HABITAT

NOTES

Arctic Loon   *Gavia arctica*

DATE   **G**18   **NG**18   **P**32

LOCALITY

HABITAT

NOTES

Common Loon   *Gavia immer*

DATE   **G**18   **NG**18   **P**32

LOCALITY

HABITAT

NOTES

Yellow-billed Loon   *Gavia adamsii*

DATE   **G**18   **NG**18   **P**32

LOCALITY

HABITAT

NOTES

G = Golden   **NG** = National Geographic   **P** = Peterson

Least Grebe   *Tachybaptus dominicus*

DATE   **G**20   **NG**22   **P**298

LOCALITY

HABITAT

NOTES

Grebes
(Podicipedidae)

Pied-billed Grebe   *Podilymbus podiceps*

DATE   **G**20   **NG**22   **P**34

LOCALITY

HABITAT

NOTES

Horned Grebe   *Podiceps auritus*

DATE   **G**20   **NG**22   **P**34

LOCALITY

HABITAT

NOTES

Red-necked Grebe   *Podiceps grisegena*

DATE   **G**20   **NG**20   **P**34

LOCALITY

HABITAT

NOTES

G = Golden   **NG** = National Geographic   **P** = Peterson

Eared Grebe   *Podiceps nigricollis*

DATE
G20	**NG**22	**P**34

LOCALITY

HABITAT

NOTES

Western Grebe   *Aechmophorus occidentalis*

DATE
G20	**NG**20	**P**34

LOCALITY

HABITAT

NOTES

PROCELLARIIFORMES

Albatrosses
(Diomedeidae)

Short-tailed Albatross   *Diomedea albatrus*

DATE
G—	**NG**24	**P**—

LOCALITY

HABITAT

NOTES

Black-footed Albatross   *Diomedea nigripes*

DATE
G22	**NG**24	**P**—

LOCALITY

HABITAT

NOTES

G = Golden   **NG** = National Geographic   **P** = Peterson

Laysan Albatross   *Diomedea immutabilis*

DATE   **G**22   **NG**24   **P**—

LOCALITY

HABITAT

NOTES

Black-browed Albatross   *Diomedea melanophris*

DATE   **G**—   **NG**24   **P**290

LOCALITY

HABITAT

NOTES

Shy Albatross   *Diomedea cauta*

DATE   **G**—   **NG**—   **P**—

LOCALITY

HABITAT

NOTES

Yellow-nosed Albatross   *Diomedea chlororhynchos*

DATE   **G**22   **NG**24   **P**290

LOCALITY

HABITAT

NOTES

G = Golden   **NG** = National Geographic   **P** = Peterson

Fulmars, Shearwaters and Petrels (*Procellariidae*)

Northern Fulmar   *Fulmarus glacialis*

DATE
                                                  G24   NG26   P76

LOCALITY

HABITAT

NOTES

Black-capped Petrel   *Pterodroma hasitata*

DATE
  G28   NG32   P76

LOCALITY

HABITAT

NOTES

Mottled Petrel   *Pterodroma inexpectata*

DATE
  G28   NG32   P292

LOCALITY

HABITAT

NOTES

Streaked Shearwater   *Calonectris leucomelas*

DATE
  G26   NG30   P—

LOCALITY

HABITAT

NOTES

G = Golden   **NG** = National Geographic   **P** = Peterson

Cory's Shearwater   *Calonectris diomedea*

DATE   G24   NG28   P74

LOCALITY

HABITAT

NOTES

Pink-footed Shearwater   *Puffinus creatopus*

DATE   G24   NG30   P—

LOCALITY

HABITAT

NOTES

Flesh-footed Shearwater   *Puffinus carneipes*

DATE   G26   NG26   P—

LOCALITY

HABITAT

NOTES

Greater Shearwater   *Puffinus gravis*

DATE   G24   NG28   P74

LOCALITY

HABITAT

NOTES

G = Golden   **NG** = National Geographic   **P** = Peterson

Buller's Shearwater　　　　　　　*Puffinus bulleri*

DATE

G26　　NG30　　P—

LOCALITY

HABITAT

NOTES

Sooty Shearwater　　　　　　　*Puffinus griseus*

DATE

G26　　NG26　　P74

LOCALITY

HABITAT

NOTES

Short-tailed Shearwater　　　　　*Puffinus tenuirostris*

DATE

G26　　NG26　　P—

LOCALITY

HABITAT

NOTES

Manx Shearwater　　　　　　　*Puffinus puffinus*

DATE

G28　　NG28　　P74

LOCALITY

HABITAT

NOTES

G = Golden　　**NG** = National Geographic　　**P** = Peterson

Black-vented Shearwater   *Puffinus opisthomelas*

DATE
                                    G28   NG30   P—

LOCALITY

HABITAT

NOTES

Little Shearwater   *Puffinus assimilis*

DATE
                                    G—   NG28   P292

LOCALITY

HABITAT

NOTES

Audubon's Shearwater   *Puffinus iherminieri*

DATE
                                    G28   NG28   P74

LOCALITY

HABITAT

NOTES

Wilson's Storm-Petrel   *Oceanites oceanicus*

DATE
                                    G30   NG34   P76

LOCALITY

HABITAT

NOTES

Storm-Petrels
(Hydrobatidae)

White-faced Storm-Petrel   *Pelagodroma marina*
DATE
G—   NG34   P292

LOCALITY

HABITAT

NOTES

British Storm-Petrel   *Hydrobates pelagicus*
DATE
G—   NG—   P292

LOCALITY

HABITAT

NOTES

Fork-tailed Storm-Petrel   *Oceanodroma furcata*
DATE
G30   NG36   P—

LOCALITY

HABITAT

NOTES

Leach's Storm-Petrel   *Oceanodroma leucorhoa*
DATE
G30   NG34   P76

LOCALITY

HABITAT

NOTES

G = Golden   **NG** = National Geographic   **P** = Peterson

Ashy Storm-Petrel   *Oceanodroma homochroa*

DATE   G30   NG36   P—

LOCALITY

HABITAT

NOTES

Band-rumped Storm-Petrel   *Oceanodroma castro*

DATE   G30   NG34   P292

LOCALITY

HABITAT

NOTES

Wedge-rumped Storm-Petrel   *Oceanodroma tethys*

DATE   G—   NG36   P—

LOCALITY

HABITAT

NOTES

Black Storm-Petrel   *Oceanodroma melania*

DATE   G30   NG36   P—

LOCALITY

HABITAT

NOTES

G = Golden   **NG** = National Geographic   **P** = Peterson

Least Storm-Petrel   *Oceanodroma microsoma*

DATE   **G**30   **NG**36   **P**—

LOCALITY

HABITAT

NOTES

Tropicbirds (Phaethontidae)

White-tailed Tropicbird   *Phaethon lepturus*

DATE   **G**32   **NG**38   **P**80

LOCALITY

HABITAT

NOTES

Red-billed Tropicbird   *Phaethon aethereus*

DATE   **G**32   **NG**38   **P**290

LOCALITY

HABITAT

NOTES

Red-tailed Tropicbird   *Phaethon rubricauda*

DATE   **G**—   **NG**38   **P**—

LOCALITY

HABITAT

NOTES

G = Golden   **NG** = National Geographic   **P** = Peterson

Masked Booby   *Sula dactylatra*

DATE
                                    G34   NG42   P80

LOCALITY

Boobies and
Gannets *(Sulidae)*

HABITAT

NOTES

Blue-footed Booby   *Sula nebouxii*

DATE
                                    G34   NG42   P—

LOCALITY

HABITAT

NOTES

Brown Booby   *Sula leucogaster*

DATE
                                    G34   NG42   P80

LOCALITY

HABITAT

NOTES

Red-footed Booby   *Sula sula*

DATE
                                    G34   NG42   P290

LOCALITY

HABITAT

NOTES

Northern Gannet — *Sula bassanus*

DATE   G34   NG40   P80

LOCALITY

HABITAT

NOTES

**Pelicans
(Pelecanidae)**

American White Pelican — *Pelecanus erythrorhynchos*

DATE   G32   NG40   P78

LOCALITY

HABITAT

NOTES

Brown Pelican — *Pelecanus occidentalis*

DATE   G32   NG40   P78

LOCALITY

HABITAT

NOTES

**Cormorants
(Phalacrocora-
cidae)**

Great Cormorant — *Phalacrocorax carbo*

DATE   G36   NG44   P40

LOCALITY

HABITAT

NOTES

G = Golden   **NG** = National Geographic   **P** = Peterson

Double-crested Cormorant   *Phalacrocorax auritus*

DATE
                                        G36   **NG**46   **P**40

LOCALITY

HABITAT

NOTES

Olivaceous Cormorant   *Phalacrocorax olivaceus*

DATE
                                        G36   **NG**44   **P**40

LOCALITY

HABITAT

NOTES

Brandt's Cormorant   *Phalacrocorax penicillatus*

DATE
                                        G36   **NG**46   **P**—

LOCALITY

HABITAT

NOTES

Pelagic Cormorant   *Phalacrocorax pelagicus*

DATE
                                        G36   **NG**46   **P**—

LOCALITY

HABITAT

NOTES

G = Golden   **NG** = National Geographic   **P** = Peterson

Red-faced Cormorant			*Phalacrocorax urile*
DATE	G36	NG46	P—
LOCALITY			
HABITAT			
NOTES			

Anhingas
(Anhingidae)

Anhinga			*Anhinga anhinga*
DATE	G36	NG44	P40
LOCALITY			
HABITAT			
NOTES			

Frigatebirds
(Fregatidae)

Magnificent Frigatebird			*Fregata magnificens*
DATE	G34	NG38	P78
LOCALITY			
HABITAT			
NOTES			

Great Frigatebird			*Fregata minor*
DATE	G—	NG—	P—
LOCALITY			
HABITAT			
NOTES			

G = Golden   **NG** = National Geographic   **P** = Peterson

Lesser Frigatebird   *Fregata ariel*

DATE

                  G—   NG—   P290

LOCALITY

HABITAT

NOTES

CICONIIFORMES

American Bittern   *Botaurus lentiginosus*

DATE

                  G98   NG48   P104

LOCALITY

HABITAT

NOTES

Bitterns and Herons *(Ardeidae)*

Least Bittern   *Ixobrychus exilis*

DATE

                  G98   NG48   P104

LOCALITY

HABITAT

NOTES

Great Blue Heron   *Ardea herodias*

DATE

                  G96   NG54   P100

LOCALITY

HABITAT

NOTES

Great Egret   *Casmerodius albus*
DATE
                                                  G94   NG52   P102
LOCALITY

HABITAT

NOTES

Chinese Egret   *Egretta eulophotes*
DATE
                                                  G—   NG—   P—
LOCALITY

HABITAT

NOTES

Little Egret   *Egretta garzetta*
DATE
                                                  G—   NG—   P294
LOCALITY

HABITAT

NOTES

Snowy Egret   *Egretta thula*
DATE
                                                  G94   NG52   P102
LOCALITY

HABITAT

NOTES

G = Golden   NG = National Geographic   P = Peterson

Little Blue Heron   *Egretta caerulea*

DATE

          G96   **NG**50   **P**100

LOCALITY

HABITAT

NOTES

Tricolored Heron   *Egretta tricolor*

DATE

          G96   **NG**50   **P**100

LOCALITY

HABITAT

NOTES

Reddish Egret   *Egretta rufescens*

DATE

          G96   **NG**50   **P**100

LOCALITY

HABITAT

NOTES

Cattle Egret   *Bubulcus ibis*

DATE

          G94   **NG**52   **P**102

LOCALITY

HABITAT

NOTES

G = Golden   **NG** = National Geographic   **P** = Peterson

Green-backed Heron   *Butorides striatus*

DATE   **G**96   **NG**50   **P**104

LOCALITY

HABITAT

NOTES

Black-crowned Night-Heron   *Nycticorax nycticorax*

DATE   **G**98   **NG**48   **P**104

LOCALITY

HABITAT

NOTES

Yellow-crowned Night-Heron   *Nycticorax violaceus*

DATE   **G**98   **NG**48   **P**104

LOCALITY

HABITAT

NOTES

**Ibises and
Spoonbills
(*Threskiorni-
thidae*)**

White Ibis   *Eudocimus albus*

DATE   **G**100   **NG**56   **P**108

LOCALITY

HABITAT

NOTES

G = Golden   **NG** = National Geographic   **P** = Peterson

Scarlet Ibis   *Eudocimus ruber*

DATE   G100   NG56   P110

LOCALITY

HABITAT

NOTES

Glossy Ibis   *Plegadis falcinellus*

DATE   G100   NG56   P108

LOCALITY

HABITAT

NOTES

White-faced Ibis   *Plegadis chihi*

DATE   G100   NG56   P108

LOCALITY

HABITAT

NOTES

Roseate Spoonbill   *Ajaia ajaja*

DATE   G100   NG56   P110

LOCALITY

HABITAT

NOTES

G = Golden   **NG** = National Geographic   **P** = Peterson

Storks
(Ciconiidae)

Jabiru — *Jabiru mycteria*
DATE
G—   NG54   P—

LOCALITY

HABITAT

NOTES

Wood Stork — *Mycteria americana*
DATE
G100   NG54   P106

LOCALITY

HABITAT

NOTES

Flamingos
(Phoenicop-
teridae)

Greater Flamingo — *Phoenicopterus ruber*
DATE
G100   NG54   P110

LOCALITY

HABITAT

NOTES

Swans, Geese and
Ducks (Anatidae)

Fulvous Whistling-Duck — *Dendrocygna bicolor*
DATE
G52   NG76   P48

LOCALITY

HABITAT

NOTES

G = Golden   NG = National Geographic   P = Peterson

Black-bellied Whistling-Duck   *Dendrocygna autumnalis*

DATE

G52   NG76   P298

LOCALITY

HABITAT

NOTES

Tundra Swan   *Cygnus columbianus*

DATE

G40   NG60   P42

LOCALITY

HABITAT

NOTES

Whooper Swan   *Cygnus cygnus*

DATE

G40   NG60   P296

LOCALITY

HABITAT

NOTES

Trumpeter Swan   *Cygnus buccinator*

DATE

G40   NG60   P42

LOCALITY

HABITAT

NOTES

Mute Swan   *Cygnus olor*

DATE   G40   NG60   P42

LOCALITY

HABITAT

NOTES

Bean Goose   *Anser fabalis*

DATE   G44   NG62   P296

LOCALITY

HABITAT

NOTES

Pink-footed Goose   *Anser brachyrhynchus*

DATE   G44   NG62   P296

LOCALITY

HABITAT

NOTES

Lesser White-fronted Goose   *Anser erythropus*

DATE   G—   NG—   P296

LOCALITY

HABITAT

NOTES

G = Golden   NG = National Geographic   P = Peterson

Greater White-fronted Goose · *Anser albifrons*

DATE   **G**44   **NG**62   **P**44

LOCALITY

HABITAT

NOTES

Snow Goose · *Chen caerulescens*

DATE   **G**44   **NG**64   **P**42

LOCALITY

HABITAT

NOTES

Ross' Goose · *Chen rossii*

DATE   **G**44   **NG**64   **P**42

LOCALITY

HABITAT

NOTES

Emperor Goose · *Chen canagica*

DATE   **G**42   **NG**64   **P**—

LOCALITY

HABITAT

NOTES

Brant   *Branta bernicla*

DATE
                                              G42   **NG**66   **P**44

LOCALITY

HABITAT

NOTES

Barnacle Goose   *Branta leucopsis*

DATE
                                              G42   **NG**66   **P**44

LOCALITY

HABITAT

NOTES

Canada Goose   *Branta canadensis*

DATE
                                              G42   **NG**66   **P**44

LOCALITY

HABITAT

NOTES

Wood Duck   *Aix sponsa*

DATE
                                              G52   **NG**78   **P**50

LOCALITY

HABITAT

NOTES

G = Golden   **NG** = National Geographic   **P** = Peterson

Green-winged Teal   *Anas crecca*

DATE
G50   NG70   P52

LOCALITY

HABITAT

NOTES

Baikal Teal   *Anas formosa*

DATE
G50   NG70   P296

LOCALITY

HABITAT

NOTES

Falcated Teal   *Anas falcata*

DATE
G50   NG70   P—

LOCALITY

HABITAT

NOTES

American Black Duck   *Anas rubripes*

DATE
G46   NG68   P48

LOCALITY

HABITAT

NOTES

G = Golden   **NG** = National Geographic   **P** = Peterson

Mottled Duck   *Anas fulvigula*

DATE   G46   NG68   P48

LOCALITY

HABITAT

NOTES

Mallard   *Anas platyrhynchos*

DATE   G46   NG68   P48

LOCALITY

HABITAT

NOTES

Spot-billed Duck   *Anas poecilorhyncha*

DATE   G—   NG68   P302

LOCALITY

HABITAT

NOTES

White-cheeked Pintail   *Anas bahamensis*

DATE   G48   NG72   P298

LOCALITY

HABITAT

NOTES

Northern Pintail   *Anas acuta*

DATE _____   G48   **NG**72   P50

LOCALITY _____

HABITAT _____

NOTES _____

_____

Garganey   *Anas querquedula*

DATE _____   G50   **NG**74   P296

LOCALITY _____

HABITAT _____

NOTES _____

_____

Blue-winged Teal   *Anas discors*

DATE _____   G50   **NG**74   P52

LOCALITY _____

HABITAT _____

NOTES _____

_____

Cinnamon Teal   *Anas cyanoptera*

DATE _____   G50   **NG**74   P52

LOCALITY _____

HABITAT _____

NOTES _____

_____

G = Golden   **NG** = National Geographic   **P** = Peterson

Northern Shoveler   *Anas clypeata*

DATE
                                        G50   **NG**74   **P**52

LOCALITY

HABITAT

NOTES

Gadwall   *Anas strepera*

DATE
                                        G48   **NG**70   **P**48

LOCALITY

HABITAT

NOTES

Eurasian Wigeon   *Anas penelope*

DATE
                                        G48   **NG**72   **P**50

LOCALITY

HABITAT

NOTES

American Wigeon   *Anas americana*

DATE
                                        G48   **NG**72   **P**50

LOCALITY

HABITAT

NOTES

G = Golden   **NG** = National Geographic   **P** = Peterson

Common Pochard
Aythya ferina

DATE   G54   NG78   P—

LOCALITY

HABITAT

NOTES

Canvasback
Aythya valisineria

DATE   G54   NG78   P58

LOCALITY

HABITAT

NOTES

Redhead
Aythya americana

DATE 3rd January 1992   G54   NG78   P58

LOCALITY Lake Tahannase LongBranch N.J.

HABITAT Freshwater Lake

NOTES A Single Male amongst a large flock of Canvasback

Ring-necked Duck
Aythya collaris

DATE   G54   NG80   P58

LOCALITY

HABITAT

NOTES

Tufted Duck   *Aythya fuligula*

DATE

G54   NG80   P296

LOCALITY

HABITAT

NOTES

Greater Scaup   *Aythya marila*

DATE

G54   NG80   P58

LOCALITY

HABITAT

NOTES

Lesser Scaup   *Aythya affinis*

DATE

G54   NG80   P58

LOCALITY

HABITAT

NOTES

Common Eider   *Somateria mollissima*

DATE

G58   NG82   P56

LOCALITY

HABITAT

NOTES

G = Golden   **NG** = National Geographic   **P** = Peterson

King Eider   *Somateria spectabilis*

DATE

          G58   NG82   P56

LOCALITY

HABITAT

NOTES

Spectacled Eider   *Somateria fischeri*

DATE

          G58   NG82   P—

LOCALITY

HABITAT

NOTES

Steller's Eider   *Polysticta stelleri*

DATE

          G58   NG82   P—

LOCALITY

HABITAT

NOTES

Harlequin Duck   *Histrionicus histrionicus*

DATE

          G56   NG84   P56

LOCALITY

HABITAT

NOTES

G = Golden   NG = National Geographic   P = Peterson

Oldsquaw   *Clangula hyemalis*
DATE
                                        G60   NG86   P56
LOCALITY

HABITAT

NOTES

Black Scoter   *Melanitta nigra*
DATE
                                        G60   NG84   P54
LOCALITY

HABITAT

NOTES

Surf Scoter   *Melanitta perspicillata*
DATE
                                        G60   NG84   P54
LOCALITY

HABITAT

NOTES

White-winged Scoter   *Melanitta fusca*
DATE
                                        G60   NG84   P54
LOCALITY

HABITAT

NOTES

G = Golden   **NG** = National Geographic   **P** = Peterson

Common Goldeneye   *Bucephala clangula*

DATE _____   G56   NG86   P60

LOCALITY _____

HABITAT _____

NOTES _____

_____

Barrow's Goldeneye   *Bucephala islandica*

DATE _____   G56   NG86   P60

LOCALITY _____

HABITAT _____

NOTES _____

_____

Bufflehead   *Bucephala albeola*

DATE _____   G56   NG86   P60

LOCALITY _____

HABITAT _____

NOTES _____

_____

Smew   *Mergellus albellus*

DATE _____   G62   NG88   P296

LOCALITY _____

HABITAT _____

NOTES _____

_____

Hooded Merganser   *Lophodytes cucullatus*

DATE
                                                    G62   NG88   P62

LOCALITY

HABITAT

NOTES

Common Merganser   *Mergus merganser*

DATE
                                                    G62   NG88   P62

LOCALITY

HABITAT

NOTES

Red-breasted Merganser   *Mergus serrator*

DATE
                                                    G62   NG88   P62

LOCALITY

HABITAT

NOTES

Ruddy Duck   *Oxyura jamaicensis*

DATE
                                                    G62   NG76   P60

LOCALITY

HABITAT

NOTES

Masked Duck
Oxyura dominica

DATE

G62   NG76   P298

LOCALITY

HABITAT

NOTES

Black Vulture
Coragyps atratus

DATE

G66   NG182   P160

LOCALITY

HABITAT

NOTES

American Vultures (Cathartidae)

Turkey Vulture
Cathartes aura

DATE

G66   NG182   P160

LOCALITY

HABITAT

NOTES

California Condor
Gymnogyps californianus

DATE

G66   NG182   P—

LOCALITY

HABITAT

NOTES

G = Golden   NG = National Geographic   P = Peterson

Ospreys, Kites, Eagles and Hawks (Accipitridae)

Osprey   *Pandion haliaetus*

DATE

                                                    G78   NG200   P158

LOCALITY

HABITAT

NOTES

Hook-billed Kite   *Chondrohierax uncinatus*

DATE

                                                    G68   NG188   P—

LOCALITY

HABITAT

NOTES

American Swallow-tailed Kite   *Elanoides forficatus*

DATE

                                                    G68   NG186   P150

LOCALITY

HABITAT

NOTES

Black-shouldered Kite   *Elanus caeruleus*

DATE

                                                    G68   NG186   P—

LOCALITY

HABITAT

NOTES

G = Golden   NG = National Geographic   P = Peterson

Snail Kite   *Rostrhamus sociabilis*

DATE
                                        G68   NG188   P150

LOCALITY

HABITAT

NOTES

Mississippi Kite   *Ictinia mississippiensis*

DATE
                                        G68   NG186   P150

LOCALITY

HABITAT

NOTES

Bald Eagle   *Haliaeetus leucocephalus*

DATE
                                        G78   NG184   P158

LOCALITY

HABITAT

NOTES

White-tailed Eagle   *Haliaeetus albicilla*

DATE
                                        G78   NG184   P296

LOCALITY

HABITAT

NOTES

G = Golden   **NG** = National Geographic   **P** = Peterson

Steller's Sea-Eagle   *Haliaeetus pelagicus*

DATE   G—   NG184   P—

LOCALITY   `

HABITAT

NOTES

Northern Harrier   *Circus cyaneus*

DATE   G70   NG188   P152

LOCALITY

HABITAT

NOTES

Sharp-shinned Hawk   *Accipiter striatus*

DATE   G70   NG190   P152

LOCALITY

HABITAT

NOTES

Cooper's Hawk   *Accipiter cooperii*

DATE   G70   NG190   P152

LOCALITY

HABITAT

NOTES

G = Golden   **NG** = National Geographic   **P** = Peterson

Northern Goshawk   *Accipiter gentilis*

DATE
                                   G70   NG190   P152

LOCALITY

HABITAT

NOTES

Common Black-Hawk   *Buteogallus anthracinus*

DATE
                                   G76   NG198   P298

LOCALITY

HABITAT

NOTES

Harris' Hawk   *Parabuteo unicinctus*

DATE
                                   G74   NG198   P—

LOCALITY

HABITAT

NOTES

Gray Hawk   *Buteo nitidus*

DATE
                                   G76   NG192   P—

LOCALITY

HABITAT

NOTES

G = Golden   **NG** = National Geographic   **P** = Peterson

Roadside Hawk
Buteo magnirostris

DATE
G—   NG—   P—

LOCALITY

HABITAT

NOTES

Red-shouldered Hawk
Buteo lineatus

DATE
G74   NG192   P156

LOCALITY

HABITAT

NOTES

Broad-winged Hawk
Buteo platypterus

DATE
G74   NG192   P156

LOCALITY

HABITAT

NOTES

Short-tailed Hawk
Buteo brachyurus

DATE
G76   NG198   P156

LOCALITY

HABITAT

NOTES

G = Golden   NG = National Geographic   P = Peterson

Swainson's Hawk   *Buteo swainsoni*

DATE   G74   NG194   P154

LOCALITY

HABITAT

NOTES

White-tailed Hawk   *Buteo albicaudatus*

DATE   G76   NG196   P—

LOCALITY

HABITAT

NOTES

Zone-tailed Hawk   *Buteo albonotatus*

DATE   G76   NG198   P—

LOCALITY

HABITAT

NOTES

Red-tailed Hawk   *Buteo jamaicensis*

DATE   G72   NG194   P154

LOCALITY

HABITAT

NOTES

G = Golden   NG = National Geographic   P = Peterson

Ferruginous Hawk   *Buteo regalis*

DATE
                                                G72   NG196   P154

LOCALITY

HABITAT

NOTES

Rough-legged Hawk   *Buteo lagopus*

DATE
                                                G72   NG196   P156

LOCALITY

HABITAT

NOTES

Golden Eagle   *Aquila chrysaetos*

DATE
                                                G78   NG184   P158

LOCALITY

HABITAT

NOTES

Falcons and Caracaras (Falconidae)

Crested Caracara   *Polyborus plancus*

DATE
                                                G78   NG200   P160

LOCALITY

HABITAT

NOTES

G = Golden   **NG** = National Geographic   **P** = Peterson

Eurasian Kestrel

Falco tinnunculus

DATE

G—   NG202   P296

LOCALITY

HABITAT

NOTES

American Kestrel

Falco sparverius

DATE

G80   NG202   P162

LOCALITY

HABITAT

NOTES

Merlin

Falco columbarius

DATE

G80   NG202   P162

LOCALITY

HABITAT

NOTES

Aplomado Falcon

Falco femoralis

DATE

G80   NG200   P—

LOCALITY

HABITAT

NOTES

G = Golden   **NG** = National Geographic   **P** = Peterson

Peregrine Falcon   *Falco peregrinus*

DATE   **G**80   **NG**204   **P**162

LOCALITY

HABITAT

NOTES

Gyrfalcon   *Falco rusticolus*

DATE   **G**80   **NG**204   **P**162

LOCALITY

HABITAT

NOTES

Prairie Falcon   *Falco mexicanus*

DATE   **G**80   **NG**204   **P**162

LOCALITY

HABITAT

NOTES

Chachalacas (Cracidae)

Plain Chachalaca   *Ortalis vetula*

DATE   **G**84   **NG**222   **P**302

LOCALITY

HABITAT

NOTES

G = Golden   **NG** = National Geographic   **P** = Peterson

Gray Partridge · *Perdix perdix* · GALLIFORMES

DATE _____ G92 NG220 P148

LOCALITY _____

HABITAT _____

NOTES _____

_____

Partridges, Pheasants, Grouse, Turkeys and Quail *(Phasianidae)*

Black Francolin · *Francolinus francolinus*

DATE _____ G92 NG220 P302

LOCALITY _____

HABITAT _____

NOTES _____

_____

Chukar · *Alectoris chukar*

DATE _____ G92 NG220 P302

LOCALITY _____

HABITAT _____

NOTES _____

_____

Ring-necked Pheasant · *Phasianus colchicus*

DATE _____ G92 NG222 P144

LOCALITY _____

HABITAT _____

NOTES _____

_____

Spruce Grouse   *Dendragapus canadensis*

DATE
                                                        G86   NG210   P146

LOCALITY

HABITAT

NOTES

Blue Grouse   *Dendragapus obscurus*

DATE
                                                        G86   NG210   P—

LOCALITY

HABITAT

NOTES

Willow Ptarmigan   *Lagopus lagopus*

DATE
                                                        G88   NG212   P148

LOCALITY

HABITAT

NOTES

Rock Ptarmigan   *Lagopus mutus*

DATE
                                                        G88   NG212   P148

LOCALITY

HABITAT

NOTES

G = Golden   **NG** = National Geographic   **P** = Peterson

White-tailed Ptarmigan   *Logopus leucurus*

DATE
                                         G88   NG212   P—

LOCALITY

HABITAT

NOTES

Ruffed Grouse   *Bonasa umbellus*

DATE
                                         G86   NG210   P144

LOCALITY

HABITAT

NOTES

Sage Grouse   *Centrocercus urophasianus*

DATE
                                         G86   NG214   P—

LOCALITY

HABITAT

NOTES

Greater Prairie-Chicken   *Tympanuchus cupido*

DATE
                                         G88   NG214   P146

LOCALITY

HABITAT

NOTES

Lesser Prairie-Chicken   *Tympanuchus pallidicinctus*

DATE   G88   NG214   P146

LOCALITY

HABITAT

NOTES

Sharp-tailed Grouse   *Tympanuchus phasianellus*

DATE   G86   NG214   P146

LOCALITY

HABITAT

NOTES

Wild Turkey   *Meleagris gallopavo*

DATE   G84   NG222   P144

LOCALITY

HABITAT

NOTES

Montezuma Quail   *Cyrtonyx montezumae*

DATE   G90   NG216   P—

LOCALITY

HABITAT

NOTES

G = Golden   NG = National Geographic   P = Peterson

Northern Bobwhite   *Colinus virginianus*

DATE   G92   NG216   P148

LOCALITY

HABITAT

NOTES

Scaled Quail   *Callipepla squamata*

DATE   G90   NG216   P148

LOCALITY

HABITAT

NOTES

Gambel's Quail   *Callipepla gambelii*

DATE   G90   NG218   P—

LOCALITY

HABITAT

NOTES

California Quail   *Callipepla californica*

DATE   G90   NG218   P—

LOCALITY

HABITAT

NOTES

Mountain Quail   *Oreortyx pictus*

DATE
                                          G90   **NG**218   **P**—

LOCALITY

HABITAT

NOTES

Rails, Gallinules and Coots *(Rallidae)*

Yellow Rail   *Coturnicops noveboracensis*

DATE
                                          G104   **NG**98   **P**114

LOCALITY

HABITAT

NOTES

Black Rail   *Laterallus jamaicensis*

DATE
                                          G104   **NG**98   **P**114

LOCALITY

HABITAT

NOTES

Corn Crake   *Crex crex*

DATE
                                          G104   **NG**98   **P**114

LOCALITY

HABITAT

NOTES

G = Golden   **NG** = National Geographic   **P** = Peterson

Clapper Rail   *Rallus longirostris*
DATE

G106   NG96   P112

LOCALITY

HABITAT

NOTES

King Rail   *Rallus elegans*
DATE

G106   NG96   P112

LOCALITY

HABITAT

NOTES

Virginia Rail   *Rallus limicola*
DATE

G104   NG98   P112

LOCALITY

HABITAT

NOTES

Sora   *Porzana carolina*
DATE

G104   NG98   P114

LOCALITY

HABITAT

NOTES

G = Golden   NG = National Geographic   P = Peterson

Paint-billed Crake   *Neocrex erythrops*

DATE
                                              G—   NG—   P298

LOCALITY

HABITAT

NOTES

Spotted Rail   *Pardirallus maculatus*

DATE
                                              G—   NG—   P298

LOCALITY

HABITAT

NOTES

Purple Gallinule   *Porphyrula martinica*

DATE
                                              G106   NG100   P64

LOCALITY

HABITAT

NOTES

Common Moorhen   *Gallinula chloropus*

DATE
                                              G106   NG100   P64

LOCALITY

HABITAT

NOTES

Eurasian Coot   *Fulica atra*

DATE   G—   **NG**100   **P**296

LOCALITY

HABITAT

NOTES

American Coot   *Fulica americana*

DATE   **G**106   **NG**100   **P**64

LOCALITY

HABITAT

NOTES

Caribbean Coot   *Fulica caribaea*

DATE   G—   **NG**100   **P**298

LOCALITY

HABITAT

NOTES

Limpkin   *Aramus guarauna*

DATE   **G**102   **NG**96   **P**108

LOCALITY

HABITAT

NOTES

Limpkins *(Aramidae)*

Cranes (Gruidae)

Sandhill Crane — *Grus canadensis*

G102   NG58   P106

DATE

LOCALITY

HABITAT

NOTES

Common Crane — *Grus grus*

G—   NG58   P294

DATE

LOCALITY

HABITAT

NOTES

Whooping Crane — *Grus americana*

G102   NG58   P106

DATE

LOCALITY

HABITAT

NOTES

Thick-knees (Burhinidae)

Double-striped Thick-knee — *Burhinus bistriatus*

G—   NG—   P—

DATE

LOCALITY

HABITAT

NOTES

G = Golden   NG = National Geographic   P = Peterson

Northern Lapwing *Vanellus vanellus* CHARADRIIFORMES

DATE   G110   NG108   P294

LOCALITY

HABITAT

NOTES

Plovers and Lapwings *(Charadriidae)*

Black-bellied Plover *Pluvialis squatarola*

DATE   G112   NG108   P118

LOCALITY

HABITAT

NOTES

Greater Golden Plover *Pluvialis apricaria*

DATE   G112   NG108   P294

LOCALITY

HABITAT

NOTES

Lesser Golden Plover *Pluvialis dominica*

DATE   G112   NG108   P118

LOCALITY

HABITAT

NOTES

G = Golden   **NG** = National Geographic   **P** = Peterson

Mongolian Plover   *Charadrius mongolus*

DATE

G114   NG106   P294

LOCALITY

HABITAT

NOTES

Snowy Plover   *Charadrius alexandrinus*

DATE

G114   NG104   P120

LOCALITY

HABITAT

NOTES

Wilson's Plover   *Charadrius wilsonia*

DATE

G114   NG104   P120

LOCALITY

HABITAT

NOTES

Common Ringed Plover   *Charadrius hiaticula*

DATE

G114   NG104   P120

LOCALITY

HABITAT

NOTES

Semipalmated Plover   *Charadrius semipalmatus*

DATE
                                            G114   **NG**104   **P**120

LOCALITY

HABITAT

NOTES

Piping Plover   *Charadrius melodus*

DATE
                                            G114   **NG**104   **P**120

LOCALITY

HABITAT

NOTES

Little Ringed Plover   *Charadrius dubius*

DATE
                                            G—   **NG**—   **P**—

LOCALITY

HABITAT

NOTES

Killdeer   *Charadrius vociferus*

DATE
                                            G114   **NG**106   **P**120

LOCALITY

HABITAT

NOTES

Mountain Plover   *Charadrius montanus*

DATE
                                            G112   NG106   P—

LOCALITY

HABITAT

NOTES

Eurasian Dotterel   *Charadrius morinellus*

DATE
                                            G112   NG106   P—

LOCALITY

HABITAT

NOTES

Oystercatchers
(Haemato-
podidae)

American Oystercatcher   *Haematopus palliatus*

DATE
                                            G110   NG102   P116

LOCALITY

HABITAT

NOTES

American Black Oystercatcher   *Haematopus bachmani*

DATE
                                            G110   NG102   P—

LOCALITY

HABITAT

NOTES

G = Golden   **NG** = National Geographic   **P** = Peterson

Black-necked Stilt   *Himantopus mexicanus*   **Stilts and Avocets**
DATE   **(*Recurviro-**
                                         G110   NG102   P116   ***stridae)***

LOCALITY

HABITAT

NOTES

American Avocet   *Recurvirostra americana*
DATE
                                         G110   NG102   P116

LOCALITY

HABITAT

NOTES

Northern Jacana   *Jacana spinosa*   **Jacanas**
DATE   **(*Jacanidae)***
                                         G110   NG102   P298

LOCALITY

HABITAT

NOTES

Common Greenshank   *Tringa nebularia*   **Sandpipers,**
DATE   **Phalaropes and**
                                         G120   NG114   P294   **Allies**
LOCALITY   **(*Scolopacidae)***

HABITAT

NOTES

G = Golden   **NG** = National Geographic   **P** = Peterson

Greater Yellowlegs   *Tringa melanoleuca*

DATE   G120   NG114   P128

LOCALITY

HABITAT

NOTES

Lesser Yellowlegs   *Tringa flavipes*

DATE   G120   NG114   P128

LOCALITY

HABITAT

NOTES

Marsh Sandpiper   *Tringa stagnatilis*

DATE   G120   NG—   P—

LOCALITY

HABITAT

NOTES

Spotted Redshank   *Tringa erythropus*

DATE   G120   NG114   P294

LOCALITY

HABITAT

NOTES

G = Golden   NG = National Geographic   P = Peterson

Wood Sandpiper   *Tringa glareola*

DATE

G120   NG118   P—

LOCALITY

HABITAT

NOTES

Solitary Sandpiper   *Tringa solitaria*

DATE

G120   NG116   P128

LOCALITY

HABITAT

NOTES

Willet   *Catoptrophorus semipalmatus*

DATE

G122   NG114   P128

LOCALITY

HABITAT

NOTES

Wandering Tattler   *Heteroscelus incanus*

DATE

G124   NG118   P—

LOCALITY

HABITAT

NOTES

G = Golden   **NG** = National Geographic   **P** = Peterson

Gray-tailed Tattler   *Heteroscelus brevipes*

DATE
                                          G124   NG118   P—

LOCALITY

HABITAT

NOTES

Common Sandpiper   *Actitis hypoleucos*

DATE
                                          G124   NG116   P—

LOCALITY

HABITAT

NOTES

Spotted Sandpiper   *Actitis macularia*

DATE
                                          G124   NG116   P132

LOCALITY

HABITAT

NOTES

Terek Sandpiper   *Xenus cinereus*

DATE
                                          G124   NG116   P—

LOCALITY

HABITAT

NOTES

G = Golden   NG = National Geographic   P = Peterson

Upland Sandpiper   *Bartramia longicauda*

DATE

                                                  G122   **NG**134   **P**130

LOCALITY

HABITAT

NOTES

Little Curlew   *Numenius minutus*

DATE

    G118   **NG**–   **P**–

LOCALITY

HABITAT

NOTES

Eskimo Curlew   *Numenius borealis*

DATE

    G118   **NG**112   **P**126

LOCALITY

HABITAT

NOTES

Whimbrel   *Numenius phaeopus*

DATE

    G118   **NG**112   **P**126

LOCALITY

HABITAT

NOTES

Bristle-thighed Curlew   *Numenius tahitiensis*

DATE
                                                      G118   **NG**112   **P**—

LOCALITY

HABITAT

NOTES

Slender-billed Curlew   *Numenius tenuirostris*

DATE
                                                      G—   **NG**—   **P**—

LOCALITY

HABITAT

NOTES

Far Eastern Curlew   *Numenius madagascariensis*

DATE
                                                      G118   **NG**112   **P**—

LOCALITY

HABITAT

NOTES

Eurasian Curlew   *Numenius arquata*

DATE
                                                      G118   **NG**112   **P**294

LOCALITY

HABITAT

NOTES

Long-billed Curlew   *Numenius americanus*

DATE   G118   NG112   P126

LOCALITY

HABITAT

NOTES

Black-tailed Godwit   *Limosa limosa*

DATE   G116   NG110   P294

LOCALITY

HABITAT

NOTES

Hudsonian Godwit   *Limosa haemastica*

DATE   G116   NG110   P126

LOCALITY

HABITAT

NOTES

Bar-tailed Godwit   *Limosa lapponica*

DATE   G116   NG110   P294

LOCALITY

HABITAT

NOTES

G = Golden   NG = National Geographic   P = Peterson

Marbled Godwit   *Limosa fedoa*

DATE
                                          G116   NG110   P126

LOCALITY

HABITAT

NOTES

Ruddy Turnstone   *Arenaria interpres*

DATE
                                          G128   NG126   P118

LOCALITY

HABITAT

NOTES

Black Turnstone   *Arenaria melanocephala*

DATE
                                          G128   NG126   P—

LOCALITY

HABITAT

NOTES

Surfbird   *Aphriza virgata*

DATE
                                          G128   NG126   P—

LOCALITY

HABITAT

NOTES

Red Knot   *Calidris canutus*

DATE

G130   NG128   P124

LOCALITY

HABITAT

NOTES

Great Knot   *Calidris tenuirostris*

DATE

G134   NG128   P—

LOCALITY

HABITAT

NOTES

Sanderling   *Calidris alba*

DATE

G130   NG128   P130

LOCALITY

HABITAT

NOTES

Semipalmated Sandpiper   *Calidris pusilla*

DATE

G132   NG130   P134

LOCALITY

HABITAT

NOTES

Western Sandpiper   *Calidris mauri*

DATE
                                             G132   **NG**130   **P**134

LOCALITY

HABITAT

NOTES

Rufous-necked Stint   *Calidris ruficollis*

DATE
    G134   **NG**132   **P**—

LOCALITY

HABITAT

NOTES

Little Stint   *Calidris minuta*

DATE
    G134   **NG**132   **P**—

LOCALITY

HABITAT

NOTES

Temminck's Stint   *Calidris temminckii*

DATE
    G134   **NG**132   **P**—

LOCALITY

HABITAT

NOTES

G = Golden   **NG** = National Geographic   **P** = Peterson

Long-toed Stint
Calidris subminuta

DATE   G134   NG132   P—

LOCALITY

HABITAT

NOTES

Least Sandpiper
Calidris minutilla

DATE   G132   NG130   P134

LOCALITY

HABITAT

NOTES

White-rumped Sandpiper
Calidris fuscicollis

DATE   G132   NG130   P134

LOCALITY

HABITAT

NOTES

Baird's Sandpiper
Calidris bairdii

DATE   G132   NG130   P134

LOCALITY

HABITAT

NOTES

G = Golden   NG = National Geographic   P = Peterson

Pectoral Sandpiper   *Calidris melanotos*

DATE

                                          G130   NG134   P130

LOCALITY

HABITAT

NOTES

Sharp-tailed Sandpiper   *Calidris acuminata*

DATE

                                          G130   NG134   P—

LOCALITY

HABITAT

NOTES

Purple Sandpiper   *Calidris maritima*

DATE

                                          G128   NG126   P132

LOCALITY

HABITAT

NOTES

Rock Sandpiper   *Calidris ptilocnemis*

DATE

                                          G128   NG126   P—

LOCALITY

HABITAT

NOTES

Dunlin   *Calidris alpina*

DATE   G130   NG128   P132

LOCALITY

HABITAT

NOTES

Curlew Sandpiper   *Calidris ferruginea*

DATE   G130   NG128   P132

LOCALITY

HABITAT

NOTES

Stilt Sandpiper   *Calidris himantopus*

DATE   G122   NG124   P132

LOCALITY

HABITAT

NOTES

Spoonbill Sandpiper   *Eurynorhynchos pygmeus*

DATE   G134   NG132   P—

LOCALITY

HABITAT

NOTES

G = Golden   NG = National Geographic   P = Peterson

Broad-billed Sandpiper · *Limicola falcinellus*

DATE

G134   NG132   P—

LOCALITY

HABITAT

NOTES

Buff-breasted Sandpiper · *Tryngites subruficollis*

DATE

G122   NG134   P130

LOCALITY

HABITAT

NOTES

Ruff · *Philomachus pugnax*

DATE

G122   NG134   P130

LOCALITY

HABITAT

NOTES

Short-billed Dowitcher · *Limnodromus griseus*

DATE

G124   NG122   P124

LOCALITY

HABITAT

NOTES

Long-billed Dowitcher *Limnodromus scolopaceus*

DATE

G124   NG122   P124

LOCALITY

HABITAT

NOTES

Jack Snipe *Lymnocryptes minimus*

DATE

G—   NG—   P294

LOCALITY

HABITAT

NOTES

Common Snipe *Gallinago gallinago*

DATE

G126   NG124   P124

LOCALITY

HABITAT

NOTES

Eurasian Woodcock *Scolopax rusticola*

DATE

G—   NG—   P294

LOCALITY

HABITAT

NOTES

American Woodcock
Scolopax minor

DATE

G126   NG124   P124

LOCALITY

HABITAT

NOTES

Wilson's Phalarope
Phalaropus tricolor

DATE

G126   NG120   P136

LOCALITY

HABITAT

NOTES

Red-necked Phalarope
Phalaropus lobatus

DATE

G126   NG120   P—

LOCALITY

HABITAT

NOTES

Red Phalarope
Phalaropus fulicaria

DATE

G126   NG120   P136

LOCALITY

HABITAT

NOTES

Skuas, Gulls, Terns, Jaegers and Skimmers *(Laridae)*

Pomarine Jaeger
Stercorarius pomarinus

DATE

G138   NG142   P82

LOCALITY

HABITAT

NOTES

Parasitic Jaeger
Stercorarius parasiticus

DATE

G138   NG142   P82

LOCALITY

HABITAT

NOTES

Long-tailed Jaeger
Stercorarius longicaudus

DATE

G138   NG142   P82

LOCALITY

HABITAT

NOTES

Great Skua
Catharacta skua

DATE

G138   NG140   P82

LOCALITY

HABITAT

NOTES

G = Golden   NG = National Geographic   P = Peterson

South Polar Skua   *Catharacta maccormicki*

DATE
                                              G138   NG140   P82

LOCALITY

HABITAT

NOTES

Laughing Gull   *Larus atricilla*

DATE
                                              G148   NG144   P88

LOCALITY

HABITAT

NOTES

Franklin's Gull   *Larus pipixcan*

DATE
                                              G148   NG144   P88

LOCALITY

HABITAT

NOTES

Little Gull   *Larus minutus*

DATE
                                              G148   NG146   P88

LOCALITY

HABITAT

NOTES

G = Golden   **NG** = National Geographic   **P** = Peterson

Common Black-headed Gull   *Larus ridibundus*

DATE
                                    G148   NG146   P88

LOCALITY

HABITAT

NOTES

Bonaparte's Gull   *Larus philadelphia*

DATE
                                    G148   NG146   P88

LOCALITY

HABITAT

NOTES

Heermann's Gull   *Larus heermanni*

DATE
                                    G146   NG144   P—

LOCALITY

HABITAT

NOTES

Mew Gull   *Larus canus*

DATE
                                    G146   NG148   P290

LOCALITY

HABITAT

NOTES

G = Golden   **NG** = National Geographic   **P** = Peterson

Ring-billed Gull   *Larus delawarensis*

DATE
                                        G146   NG148   P86

LOCALITY

HABITAT

NOTES

California Gull   *Larus californicus*

DATE
                                        G144   NG150   P86

LOCALITY

HABITAT

NOTES

Herring Gull   *Larus argentatus*

DATE
                                        G144   NG150   P86

LOCALITY

HABITAT

NOTES

Thayer's Gull   *Larus thayeri*

DATE .
                                        G144   NG152   P86

LOCALITY

HABITAT

NOTES

G = Golden   **NG** = National Geographic   **P** = Peterson

Iceland Gull   *Larus glaucoides*

DATE
                                    G140   NG152   P84

LOCALITY

HABITAT

NOTES

Lesser Black-backed Gull   *Larus fuscus*

DATE
                                    G142   NG154   P86

LOCALITY

HABITAT

NOTES

Slaty-backed Gull   *Larus schistisagus*

DATE
                                    G142   NG154   P—

LOCALITY

HABITAT

NOTES

Yellow-footed Gull   *Larus livens*

DATE
                                    G142   NG156   P—

LOCALITY

HABITAT

NOTES

G = Golden   **NG** = National Geographic   **P** = Peterson

Western Gull   *Larus occidentalis*

DATE
                                                    G142   **NG**156   **P**—

LOCALITY

HABITAT

NOTES

Glaucous-winged Gull   *Larus glaucescens*

DATE
                                                    G140   **NG**156   **P**—

LOCALITY

HABITAT

NOTES

Glaucous Gull   *Larus hyperboreus*

DATE
                                                    G140   **NG**152   **P**84

LOCALITY

HABITAT

NOTES

Great Black-backed Gull   *Larus marinus*

DATE
                                                    G142   **NG**154   **P**86

LOCALITY

HABITAT

NOTES

Black-legged Kittiwake   *Rissa tridactyla*

DATE
G146   NG158   P86

LOCALITY

HABITAT

NOTES

Red-legged Kittiwake   *Rissa brevirostris*

DATE
G146   NG158   P—

LOCALITY

HABITAT

NOTES

Ross' Gull   *Rhodostethia rosea*

DATE
G146   NG146   P84

LOCALITY

HABITAT

NOTES

Sabine's Gull   *Xema sabini*

DATE
G148   NG158   P88

LOCALITY

HABITAT

NOTES

Ivory Gull   *Pagophila eburnea*

DATE
                                           G140   NG158   P84

LOCALITY

HABITAT

NOTES

Gull-billed Tern   *Sterna nilotica*

DATE
                                           G154   NG164   P94

LOCALITY

HABITAT

NOTES

Caspian Tern   *Sterna caspia*

DATE
                                           G154   NG168   P94

LOCALITY

HABITAT

NOTES

Royal Tern   *Sterna maxima*

DATE
                                           G154   NG168   P94

LOCALITY

HABITAT

NOTES

Elegant Tern
Sterna elegans

DATE

G154   NG168   P—

LOCALITY

HABITAT

NOTES

Sandwich Tern
Sterna sandvicensis

DATE

G154   NG168   P94

LOCALITY

HABITAT

NOTES

Roseate Tern
Sterna dougallii

DATE

G152   NG164   P96

LOCALITY

HABITAT

NOTES

Common Tern
Sterna hirundo

DATE

G152   NG162   P96

LOCALITY

HABITAT

NOTES

Arctic Tern   *Sterna paradisaea*

DATE   G152   NG162   P96

LOCALITY

HABITAT

NOTES

Forster's Tern   *Sterna forsteri*

DATE   G152   NG164   P96

LOCALITY

HABITAT

NOTES

Least Tern   *Sterna antillarum*

DATE   G152   NG166   P96

LOCALITY

HABITAT

NOTES

Aleutian Tern   *Sterna aleutica*

DATE   G156   NG162   P—

LOCALITY

HABITAT

NOTES

Bridled Tern   *Sterna anaethetus*

DATE

G156   **NG**170   **P**98

LOCALITY

HABITAT

NOTES

Sooty Tern   *Sterna fuscata*

DATE

G156   **NG**170   **P**98

LOCALITY

HABITAT

NOTES

White-winged Tern   *Chlidonias leucopterus*

DATE

G156   **NG**166   **P**292

LOCALITY

HABITAT

NOTES

Black Tern   *Chlidonias niger*

DATE

G156   **NG**166   **P**98

LOCALITY

HABITAT

NOTES

G = Golden   **NG** = National Geographic   **P** = Peterson

Brown Noddy   *Anous stolidus*

DATE   G156   NG170   P98

LOCALITY

HABITAT

NOTES

Black Noddy   *Anous minutus*

DATE   G156   NG170   P98

LOCALITY

HABITAT

NOTES

Black Skimmer   *Rynchops niger*

DATE   G156   NG170   P98

LOCALITY

HABITAT

NOTES

Auks, Murres and Puffins *(Alcidae)*

Dovekie   *Alle alle*

DATE   G160   NG172   P38

LOCALITY

HABITAT

NOTES

Common Murre   *Uria aalge*
DATE
                                        G160   NG172   P36
LOCALITY

HABITAT

NOTES

Thick-billed Murre   *Uria lomvia*
DATE
                                        G160   NG172   P36
LOCALITY

HABITAT

NOTES

Razorbill   *Alca torda*
DATE
                                        G160   NG172   P36
LOCALITY

HABITAT

NOTES

Black Guillemot   *Cepphus grylle*
DATE
                                        G160   NG174   P38
LOCALITY

HABITAT

NOTES

Pigeon Guillemot   *Cepphus columba*

DATE
                                        G160   **NG**174   **P**—

LOCALITY

HABITAT

NOTES

Marbled Murrelet   *Brachyramphus marmoratus*

DATE
                                        G164   **NG**174   **P**—

LOCALITY

HABITAT

NOTES

Kittlitz's Murrelet   *Brachyramphus brevirostris*

DATE
                                        G164   **NG**174   **P**—

LOCALITY

HABITAT

NOTES

Xantus' Murrelet   *Synthliboramphus hypoleucus*

DATE
                                        G164   **NG**176   **P**—

LOCALITY

HABITAT

NOTES

G = Golden   **NG** = National Geographic   **P** = Peterson

Craveri's Murrelet   *Synthliboramphus craveri*

DATE

    G164   **NG**176   **P**—

LOCALITY

HABITAT

NOTES

Ancient Murrelet   *Synthliboramphus antiquus*

DATE

    G164   **NG**176   **P**—

LOCALITY

HABITAT

NOTES

Cassin's Auklet   *Ptychoramphys aleuticus*

DATE

    G164   **NG**176   **P**—

LOCALITY

HABITAT

NOTES

Parakeet Auklet   *Cyclorrhynchus psittacula*

DATE

    G164   **NG**178   **P**—

LOCALITY

HABITAT

NOTES

G = Golden   **NG** = National Geographic   **P** = Peterson

Least Auklet   *Aethia pusilla*

DATE
                                         G164   NG178   P—

LOCALITY

HABITAT

NOTES

Whiskered Auklet   *Aethia pygmaea*

DATE
                                         G162   NG178   P—

LOCALITY

HABITAT

NOTES

Crested Auklet   *Aethia cristatella*

DATE
                                         G162   NG178   P—

LOCALITY

HABITAT

NOTES

Rhinoceros Auklet   *Cerorhinca monocerata*

DATE
                                         G162   NG180   P—

LOCALITY

HABITAT

NOTES

Tufted Puffin
Fratercula cirrhata

DATE
                            G162   NG180   P—

LOCALITY

HABITAT

NOTES

Atlantic Puffin
Fratercula arctica

DATE
                            G162   NG180   P38

LOCALITY

HABITAT

NOTES

Horned Puffin
Fratercula corniculata

DATE
                            G162   NG180   P—

LOCALITY

HABITAT

NOTES

COLUMBIFORMES

Rock Dove
Columba livia

Pigeons and Doves *(Columbidae)*

DATE
                            G166   NG224   P180

LOCALITY

HABITAT

NOTES

G = Golden   **NG** = National Geographic   **P** = Peterson

Scaly-naped Pigeon   *Columba squamosa*

DATE
                                            G—   NG—   P298

LOCALITY

HABITAT

NOTES

White-crowned Pigeon   *Columba leucocephala*

DATE
                                            G166   NG224   P180

LOCALITY

HABITAT

NOTES

Red-billed Pigeon   *Columba flavirostris*

DATE
                                            G166   NG224   P—

LOCALITY

HABITAT

NOTES

Band-tailed Pigeon   *Columba fasciata*

DATE
                                            G166   NG224   P—

LOCALITY

HABITAT

NOTES

Ringed Turtle-Dove   *Streptopelia risoria*

DATE   G168   NG226   P180

LOCALITY

HABITAT

NOTES

Spotted Dove   *Streptopelia chinensis*

DATE   G168   NG226   P—

LOCALITY

HABITAT

NOTES

White-winged Dove   *Zenaida asiatica*

DATE   G166   NG226   P180

LOCALITY

HABITAT

NOTES

Zenaida Dove   *Zenaida aurita*

DATE   G—   NG226   P298

LOCALITY

HABITAT

NOTES

Mourning Dove   *Zenaida macroura*
DATE
                                          G166   NG226   P180
LOCALITY

HABITAT

NOTES

Inca Dove   *Columbina inca*
DATE
                                          G168   NG228   P180
LOCALITY

HABITAT

NOTES

Common Ground-Dove   *Columbina passerina*
DATE
                                          G168   NG228   P180
LOCALITY

HABITAT

NOTES

Ruddy Ground-Dove   *Columbina talpacoti*
DATE
                                          G168   NG228   P—
LOCALITY

HABITAT

NOTES

White-tipped Dove — *Leptotila verreauxi*
DATE   G168   NG228   P—

LOCALITY

HABITAT

NOTES

Key West Quail-Dove — *Geotrygon chrysia*
DATE   G—   NG228   P298

LOCALITY

HABITAT

NOTES

Ruddy Quail-Dove — *Geotrygon montana*
DATE   G—   NG228   P298

LOCALITY

HABITAT

NOTES

Budgerigar — *Melopsittacus undulatus*
DATE   G170   NG230   P178

LOCALITY

HABITAT

NOTES

PSITTACIFORMES

Parakeets and Parrots *(Psittacidae)*

G = Golden   NG = National Geographic   P = Peterson

Rose-ringed Parakeet · *Psittacula krameri*

DATE

G170   NG230   P178

LOCALITY

HABITAT

NOTES

Monk Parakeet · *Myopsitta monachus*

DATE

G170   NG230   P178

LOCALITY

HABITAT

NOTES

Thick-billed Parrot · *Rhynchopsitta pachyrhyncha*

DATE

G—   NG232   P—

LOCALITY

HABITAT

NOTES

Canary-winged Parakeet · *Brotogeris versicolurus*

DATE

G170   NG230   P178

LOCALITY

HABITAT

NOTES

G = Golden   **NG** = National Geographic   **P** = Peterson

Red-crowned Parrot   *Amazona viridigenalis*

DATE
                                      G170   **NG**232   **P**178

LOCALITY

HABITAT

NOTES

Yellow-headed Parrot   *Amazona oratrix*

DATE
                                      G170   **NG**232   **P**178

LOCALITY

HABITAT

NOTES

CUCULIFORMES

Common Cuckoo   *Cuculus canorus*

DATE
                                      G—   **NG**234   **P**—

LOCALITY

HABITAT

NOTES

Cuckoos, Roadrunners and Anis *(Cuculidae)*

Oriental Cuckoo   *Cuculus saturatus*

DATE
                                      G—   **NG**234   **P**—

LOCALITY

HABITAT

NOTES

G = Golden   **NG** = National Geographic   **P** = Peterson

Black-billed Cuckoo — *Coccyzus erythropthalmus*

DATE

G172   NG236   P182

LOCALITY

HABITAT

NOTES

Yellow-billed Cuckoo — *Coccyzus americanus*

DATE

G172   NG236   P182

LOCALITY

HABITAT

NOTES

Mangrove Cuckoo — *Coccyzus minor*

DATE

G172   NG236   P182

LOCALITY

HABITAT

NOTES

Greater Roadrunner — *Geococcyx californianus*

DATE

G172   NG236   P182

LOCALITY

HABITAT

NOTES

Smooth-billed Ani   *Crotophaga ani*

DATE
                                    G172   NG234   P182
LOCALITY

HABITAT

NOTES

Groove-billed Ani   *Crotophaga sulcirostris*

DATE
                                    G172   NG234   P182
LOCALITY

HABITAT

NOTES

STRIGIFORMES

Common Barn-Owl   *Tyto alba*

DATE
                                    G176   NG238   P174
LOCALITY

HABITAT

NOTES

Barn Owls
(Tytonidae)

Oriental Scops-Owl   *Otus sunia*

DATE
                                    G—   NG—   P—
LOCALITY

HABITAT

NOTES

Typical Owls
(Strigidae)

Flammulated Owl   *Otus flammeolus*

DATE
                                               G180   NG244   P—

LOCALITY

HABITAT

NOTES

Eastern Screech-Owl   *Otus asio*

DATE
                                               G174   NG242   P172

LOCALITY

HABITAT

NOTES

Western Screech-Owl   *Otus kennicottii*

DATE
                                               G174   NG242   P—

LOCALITY

HABITAT

NOTES

Whiskered Screech-Owl   *Otus trichopsis*

DATE
                                               G180   NG242   P—

LOCALITY

HABITAT

NOTES

G = Golden   **NG** = National Geographic   **P** = Peterson

Great Horned Owl   *Bubo virginianus*

DATE
                                          G174   NG238   P174

LOCALITY

HABITAT

NOTES

Snowy Owl   *Nyctea scandiaca*

DATE
                                          G176   NG240   P174

LOCALITY

HABITAT

NOTES

Northern Hawk-Owl   *Surnia ulula*

DATE
                                          G178   NG246   P176

LOCALITY

HABITAT

NOTES

Northern Pygmy-Owl   *Glaucidium gnoma*

DATE
                                          G180   NG244   P—

LOCALITY

HABITAT

NOTES

G = Golden   NG = National Geographic   P = Peterson

Ferruginous Pygmy-Owl   *Glaucidium brasilianum*

DATE

G180   NG244   P—

LOCALITY

HABITAT

NOTES

Elf Owl   *Micrathene whitneyi*

DATE

G180   NG244   P—

LOCALITY

HABITAT

NOTES

Burrowing Owl   *Athene cunicularia*

DATE

G178   NG246   P176

LOCALITY

HABITAT

NOTES

Spotted Owl   *Strix occidentalis*

DATE

G176   NG240   P—

LOCALITY

HABITAT

NOTES

G = Golden   NG = National Geographic   P = Peterson

Barred Owl   *Strix varia*

DATE
                                        G176   **NG**240   **P**174

LOCALITY

HABITAT

NOTES

Great Gray Owl   *Strix nebulosa*

DATE
                                        G176   **NG**240   **P**174

LOCALITY

HABITAT

NOTES

Long-eared Owl   *Asio otus*

DATE
                                        G174   **NG**238   **P**172

LOCALITY

HABITAT

NOTES

Short-eared Owl   *Asio flammeus*

DATE
                                        G174   **NG**238   **P**172

LOCALITY

HABITAT

NOTES

G = Golden   **NG** = National Geographic   **P** = Peterson

Boreal Owl   *Aegolius funereus*

DATE
                                         G178   **NG**246   **P**176

LOCALITY

HABITAT

NOTES

Northern Saw-whet Owl   *Aegolius acadicus*

DATE
    G178   **NG**246   **P**176

LOCALITY

HABITAT

NOTES

CAPRIMULGIFORMES

Goatsuckers
(Caprimulgidae)

Lesser Nighthawk   *Chordeiles acutipennis*

DATE
    G182   **NG**250   **P**184

LOCALITY

HABITAT

NOTES

Common Nighthawk   *Chordeiles minor*

DATE
    G182   **NG**250   **P**184

LOCALITY

HABITAT

NOTES

G = Golden   **NG** = National Geographic   **P** = Peterson

Antillean Nighthawk   *Chordeiles gundlachii*

DATE
                                          G182   NG250   P184

LOCALITY

HABITAT

NOTES

Common Pauraque   *Nyctidromus albicollis*

DATE
                                          G182   NG250   P—

LOCALITY

HABITAT

NOTES

Common Poorwill   *Phalaenoptilus nuttallii*

DATE
                                          G182   NG248   P184

LOCALITY

HABITAT

NOTES

Chuck-will's-widow   *Caprimulgus carolinensis*

DATE
                                          G182   NG248   P184

LOCALITY

HABITAT

NOTES

G = Golden   **NG** = National Geographic   **P** = Peterson

Buff-collared Nightjar   *Caprimulgus ridgwayi*

DATE

G182   NG248   P—

LOCALITY

HABITAT

NOTES

Whip-poor-will   *Caprimulgus vociferus*

DATE

G182   NG248   P184

LOCALITY

HABITAT

NOTES

Jungle Nightjar   *Caprimulgus indicus*

DATE

G—   NG—   P—

LOCALITY

HABITAT

NOTES

APODIFORMES

Swifts *(Apodidae)*

Black Swift   *Cypseloides niger*

DATE

G184   NG252   P—

LOCALITY

HABITAT

NOTES

G = Golden   NG = National Geographic   P = Peterson

White-collared Swift
Streptoprocne zonaris

DATE

G—   NG252   P—

LOCALITY

HABITAT

NOTES

Chimney Swift
Chaetura pelagica

DATE

G184   NG252   P204

LOCALITY

HABITAT

NOTES

Vaux's Swift
Chaetura vauxi

DATE

G184   NG252   P204

LOCALITY

HABITAT

NOTES

White-throated Needletail
Hirundapus caudacutus

DATE

G—   NG252   P—

LOCALITY

HABITAT

NOTES

G = Golden   NG = National Geographic   P = Peterson

Common Swift
Apus apus

DATE   **G**—   **NG**—   **P**—

LOCALITY

HABITAT

NOTES

Fork-tailed Swift
Apus pacificus

DATE   **G**—   **NG**252   **P**—

LOCALITY

HABITAT

NOTES

White-throated Swift
Aeronautes saxatalis

DATE   **G**184   **NG**252   **P**—

LOCALITY

HABITAT

NOTES

Antillean Palm Swift
Tachornis phoenicobia

DATE   **G**—   **NG**—   **P**300

LOCALITY

HABITAT

NOTES

G = Golden   **NG** = National Geographic   **P** = Peterson

Green Violet-ear

Colibri thalassinus

G—   NG254   P—

DATE

LOCALITY

HABITAT

NOTES

Cuban Emerald

Chlorostilbon ricordii

G188   NG254   P300

DATE

LOCALITY

HABITAT

NOTES

Broad-billed Hummingbird

Cynanthus latirostris

G190   NG256   P—

DATE

LOCALITY

HABITAT

NOTES

White-eared Hummingbird

Hylocharis leucotis

G190   NG256   P—

DATE

LOCALITY

HABITAT

NOTES

Hummingbirds
(Trochilidae)

Berylline Hummingbird   *Amazilia beryllina*

DATE

G—   NG254   P—

LOCALITY

HABITAT

NOTES

Rufous-tailed Hummingbird   *Amazilia tzacatl*

DATE

G—   NG—   P—

LOCALITY

HABITAT

NOTES

Buff-bellied Hummingbird   *Amazilia yucatanensis*

DATE

G190   NG254   P—

LOCALITY

HABITAT

NOTES

Violet-crowned Hummingbird   *Amazilia violiceps*

DATE

G190   NG256   P—

LOCALITY

HABITAT

NOTES

G = Golden   NG = National Geographic   P = Peterson

Blue-throated Hummingbird   *Lampornis clemenciae*

DATE

G190   NG256   P—

LOCALITY

HABITAT

NOTES

Magnificent Hummingbird   *Eugenes fulgens*

DATE

G190   NG256   P—

LOCALITY

HABITAT

NOTES

Plain-capped Starthroat   *Heliomaster constantii*

DATE

G—   NG256   P—

LOCALITY

HABITAT

NOTES

Bahama Woodstar   *Calliphlox evelynae*

DATE

G—   NG254   P300

LOCALITY

HABITAT

NOTES

G = Golden   NG = National Geographic   P = Peterson

Lucifer Hummingbird   *Calothorax lucifer*

DATE   G190   NG254   P—

LOCALITY

HABITAT

NOTES

Ruby-throated Hummingbird   *Archilochus colubris*

DATE   G186   NG258   P186

LOCALITY

HABITAT

NOTES

Black-chinned Hummingbird   *Archilochus alexandri*

DATE   G188   NG258   P—

LOCALITY

HABITAT

NOTES

Anna's Hummingbird   *Calypte anna*

DATE   G186   NG258   P—

LOCALITY

HABITAT

NOTES

Costa's Hummingbird   *Calypte costae*

DATE   **G**188   **NG**258   **P**—

LOCALITY

HABITAT

NOTES

Calliope Hummingbird   *Stellula calliope*

DATE   **G**186   **NG**260   **P**—

LOCALITY

HABITAT

NOTES

Bumblebee Hummingbird   *Atthis heloisa*

DATE   **G**—   **NG**—   **P**—

LOCALITY

HABITAT

NOTES

Broad-tailed Hummingbird   *Selasphorus platycercus*

DATE   **G**186   **NG**260   **P**—

LOCALITY

HABITAT

NOTES

G = Golden   **NG** = National Geographic   **P** = Peterson

Rufous Hummingbird　　　　　　　　*Selasphorus rufus*
DATE　　　　　　　　　　　　　　　G188　　NG260　　P186

LOCALITY

HABITAT

NOTES

Allen's Hummingbird　　　　　　　*Selasphorus sasin*
DATE　　　　　　　　　　　　　　　G188　　NG260　　P—

LOCALITY

HABITAT

NOTES

TROGONIFORMES

Trogons
(Trogonidae)

Elegant Trogon　　　　　　　　　　*Trogon elegans*
DATE　　　　　　　　　　　　　　　G192　　NG232　　P—

LOCALITY

HABITAT

NOTES

Eared Trogon　　　　　　　　　*Euptilotus neoxenus*
DATE　　　　　　　　　　　　　　　G192　　NG232　　P—

LOCALITY

HABITAT

NOTES

Hoopoe   *Upupa epops*

DATE   **G**–   **NG**–   **P**–

LOCALITY

HABITAT

NOTES

CORACIIFORMES

Hoopoes
(Upupidae)

Ringed Kingfisher   *Ceryle torquata*

DATE   **G**192   **NG**262   **P**–

LOCALITY

HABITAT

NOTES

Kingfishers
(Alcedinidae)

Belted Kingfisher   *Ceryle alcyon*

DATE   **G**192   **NG**262   **P**186

LOCALITY

HABITAT

NOTES

Green Kingfisher   *Chloroceryle americana*

DATE   **G**192   **NG**262   **P**–

LOCALITY

HABITAT

NOTES

PICIFORMES

Woodpeckers and Allies *(Picidae)*

Eurasian Wryneck   *Jynx torquilla*

DATE   G—   NG—   P—

LOCALITY

HABITAT

NOTES

Lewis' Woodpecker   *Melanerpes lewis*

DATE   G198   NG266   P—

LOCALITY

HABITAT

NOTES

Red-headed Woodpecker   *Melanerpes erythrocephalus*

DATE   G198   NG266   P188

LOCALITY

HABITAT

NOTES

Acorn Woodpecker   *Melanerpes formicivorus*

DATE   G198   NG266   P—

LOCALITY

HABITAT

NOTES

G = Golden   NG = National Geographic   P = Peterson

Gila Woodpecker　　　　　　　*Melanerpes uropygialis*

DATE

G196　　　NG264　　　P—

LOCALITY

HABITAT

NOTES

Golden-fronted Woodpecker　　*Melanerpes aurifrons*

DATE

G196　　　NG264　　　P—

LOCALITY

HABITAT

NOTES

Red-bellied Woodpecker　　　*Melanerpes carolinus*

DATE

G196　　　NG264　　　P190

LOCALITY

HABITAT

NOTES

Yellow-bellied Sapsucker　　　*Sphyrapicus varius*

DATE

G198　　　NG268　　　P190

LOCALITY

HABITAT

NOTES

G = Golden　　NG = National Geographic　　P = Peterson

Red-breasted Sapsucker   *Sphyrapicus ruber*

DATE
                                          G198   **NG**268   **P**—

LOCALITY

HABITAT

NOTES

Williamson's Sapsucker   *Sphyrapicus thyroideus*

DATE
                                          G198   **NG**268   **P**—

LOCALITY

HABITAT

NOTES

Ladder-backed Woodpecker   *Picoides scalaris*

DATE
                                          G196   **NG**272   **P**—

LOCALITY

HABITAT

NOTES

Nuttall's Woodpecker   *Picoides nuttallii*

DATE
                                          G196   **NG**272   **P**—

LOCALITY

HABITAT

NOTES

Downy Woodpecker   *Picoides pubescens*

DATE
                                    G200   **NG**270   **P**192

LOCALITY

HABITAT

NOTES

Hairy Woodpecker   *Picoides villosus*

DATE
                                    G200   **NG**270   **P**192

LOCALITY

HABITAT

NOTES

Strickland's Woodpecker   *Picoides stricklandi*

DATE
                                    G200   **NG**272   **P**—

LOCALITY

HABITAT

NOTES

Red-cockaded Woodpecker   *Picoides borealis*

DATE
                                    G196   **NG**272   **P**190

LOCALITY

HABITAT

NOTES

White-headed Woodpecker   *Picoides albolarvatus*

DATE
                                                    G198   NG266   P—

LOCALITY

HABITAT

NOTES

Three-toed Woodpecker   *Picoides tridactylus*

DATE
                                                    G200   NG270   P192

LOCALITY

HABITAT

NOTES

Black-backed Woodpecker   *Picoides arcticus*

DATE
                                                    G200   NG270   P192

LOCALITY

HABITAT

NOTES

Northern Flicker   *Colaptes auratus*

DATE
                                                    G194   NG264   P190

LOCALITY

HABITAT

NOTES

G = Golden   **NG** = National Geographic   **P** = Peterson

Pileated Woodpecker *Dryocopus pileatus*

DATE

G194   NG274   P188

LOCALITY

HABITAT

NOTES

Ivory-billed Woodpecker *Campephilus principalis*

DATE

G194   NG274   P188

LOCALITY

HABITAT

NOTES

PASSERIFORMES

Northern Beardless-Tyrannulet *Camptostoma imberbe*

Tyrant Flycatchers *(Tyrannidae)*

DATE

G214   NG292   P—

LOCALITY

HABITAT

NOTES

Olive-sided Flycatcher *Contopus borealis*

DATE

G216   NG284   P196

LOCALITY

HABITAT

NOTES

Greater Pewee   *Contopus pertinax*

DATE
                                          G216   **NG**284   **P**—

LOCALITY

HABITAT

NOTES

Western Wood-Pewee   *Contopus sordidulus*

DATE
                                          G216   **NG**284   **P**—

LOCALITY

HABITAT

NOTES

Eastern Wood-Pewee   *Contopus virens*

DATE
                                          G216   **NG**284   **P**196

LOCALITY

HABITAT

NOTES

Yellow-bellied Flycatcher   *Empidonax flaviventris*

DATE
                                          G212   **NG**292   **P**198

LOCALITY

HABITAT

NOTES

G = Golden   **NG** = National Geographic   **P** = Peterson

Acadian Flycatcher
Empidonax virescens

DATE
G212   NG290   P198

LOCALITY

HABITAT

NOTES

Alder Flycatcher
Empidonax alnorum

DATE
G212   NG290   P198

LOCALITY

HABITAT

NOTES

Willow Flycatcher
Empidonax traillii

DATE
G212   NG290   P198

LOCALITY

HABITAT

NOTES

Least Flycatcher
Empidonax minimus

DATE
G212   NG290   P198

LOCALITY

HABITAT

NOTES

G = Golden   NG = National Geographic   P = Peterson

Hammond's Flycatcher   *Empidonax hammondii*

DATE
                                    G214   NG288   P—

LOCALITY

HABITAT

NOTES

Dusky Flycatcher   *Empidonax oberholseri*

DATE
                                    G214   NG288   P—

LOCALITY

HABITAT

NOTES

Gray Flycatcher   *Empidonax wrightii*

DATE
                                    G214   NG288   P—

LOCALITY

HABITAT

NOTES

Western Flycatcher   *Empidonax difficilis*

DATE
                                    G214   NG292   P—

LOCALITY

HABITAT

NOTES

G = Golden   **NG** = National Geographic   **P** = Peterson

Buff-breasted Flycatcher   *Empidonax fulvifrons*

DATE   G214   NG292   P—

LOCALITY

HABITAT

NOTES

Black Phoebe   *Sayornis nigricans*

DATE   G210   NG286   P—

LOCALITY

HABITAT

NOTES

Eastern Phoebe   *Sayornis phoebe*

DATE   G210   NG286   P196

LOCALITY

HABITAT

NOTES

Say's Phoebe   *Sayornis saya*

DATE   G210   NG286   P196

LOCALITY

HABITAT

NOTES

Vermilion Flycatcher   *Pyrocephalus rubinus*

DATE
                                        G204   **NG**286   **P**196

LOCALITY

HABITAT

NOTES

Dusky-capped Flycatcher   *Myiarchus tuberculifer*

DATE
                                        G208   **NG**282   **P**—

LOCALITY

HABITAT

NOTES

Ash-throated Flycatcher   *Myiarchus cinerascens*

DATE
                                        G208   **NG**282   **P**194

LOCALITY

HABITAT

NOTES

Great Crested Flycatcher   *Myiarchus crinitus*

DATE
                                        G208   **NG**282   **P**194

LOCALITY

HABITAT

NOTES

G = Golden   **NG** = National Geographic   **P** = Peterson

Brown-crested Flycatcher   *Myiarchus tyrannulus*

DATE
                                              G208   NG282   P—

LOCALITY

HABITAT

NOTES

Great Kiskadee   *Pitangus sulphuratus*

DATE
                                              G204   NG280   P300

LOCALITY

HABITAT

NOTES

La Sagra's Flycatcher   *Myiarchus sagrae*

DATE
                                              G—   NG—   P—

LOCALITY

HABITAT

NOTES

Sulphur-bellied Flycatcher   *Myiodynastes luteiventris*

DATE
                                              G204   NG280   P—

LOCALITY

HABITAT

NOTES

Variegated Flycatcher   *Empidonomus varius*

DATE
                                    G—   **NG**280   **P**300

LOCALITY

HABITAT

NOTES

Tropical Kingbird   *Tyrannus melancholicus*

DATE
                                    G206   **NG**278   **P**300

LOCALITY

HABITAT

NOTES

Couch's Kingbird   *Tyrannus couchii*

DATE
                                    G206   **NG**278   **P**—

LOCALITY

HABITAT

NOTES

Cassin's Kingbird   *Tyrannus vociferans*

DATE
                                    G206   **NG**278   **P**—

LOCALITY

HABITAT

NOTES

Thick-billed Kingbird · *Tyrannus crassirostris*

DATE

G206   NG276   P—

LOCALITY

HABITAT

NOTES

Western Kingbird · *Tyrannus verticalis*

DATE

G206   NG278   P194

LOCALITY

HABITAT

NOTES

Eastern Kingbird · *Tyrannus tyrannus*

DATE

G206   NG276   P194

LOCALITY

HABITAT

NOTES

Gray Kingbird · *Tyrannus dominicensis*

DATE

G206   NG276   P194

LOCALITY

HABITAT

NOTES

Loggerhead Kingbird   *Tyrannus caudifasciatus*

DATE
                                              G—   **NG**276   **P**300

LOCALITY

HABITAT

NOTES

Scissor-tailed Flycatcher   *Tyrannus forficatus*

DATE
                                              G204   **NG**280   **P**194

LOCALITY

HABITAT

NOTES

Fork-tailed Flycatcher   *Tyrannus savana*

DATE
                                              G204   **NG**280   **P**300

LOCALITY

HABITAT

NOTES

Rose-throated Becard   *Pachyramphus aglaiae*

DATE
                                              G204   **NG**294   **P**—

LOCALITY

HABITAT

NOTES

G = Golden   **NG** = National Geographic   **P** = Peterson

Eurasian Skylark
Alauda arvensis
Larks *(Alaudidae)*

DATE

G218   **NG**294   P—

LOCALITY

HABITAT

NOTES

Horned Lark
Eremophila alpestris

DATE

G218   **NG**294   P200

LOCALITY

HABITAT

NOTES

Purple Martin
Progne subis
Swallows *(Hirundinidae)*

DATE

G220   **NG**296   P202

LOCALITY

HABITAT

NOTES

Cuban Martin
Progne cryptoleuca

DATE

G—   **NG**—   P300

LOCALITY

HABITAT

NOTES

Gray-breasted Martin   *Progne chalybea*
DATE   G—   NG—   P300

LOCALITY

HABITAT

NOTES

Southern Martin   *Progne elegans*
DATE   G—   NG—   P—

LOCALITY

HABITAT

NOTES

Tree Swallow   *Tachycineta bicolor*
DATE   G220   NG296   P204

LOCALITY

HABITAT

NOTES

Violet-green Swallow   *Tachycineta thalassina*
DATE   G220   NG296   P—

LOCALITY

HABITAT

NOTES

G = Golden   NG = National Geographic   P = Peterson

Bahama Swallow
Tachycineta cyaneoviridis

DATE

G220   NG296   P300

LOCALITY

HABITAT

NOTES

Northern Rough-winged Swallow
Stelgidopteryx serripennis

DATE

G220   NG298   P—

LOCALITY

HABITAT

NOTES

Bank Swallow
Riparia riparia

DATE

G220   NG298   P204

LOCALITY

HABITAT

NOTES

Cliff Swallow
Hirundo pyrrhonota

DATE

G218   NG298   P202

LOCALITY

HABITAT

NOTES

G = Golden   NG = National Geographic   P = Peterson

Cave Swallow   *Hirundo fulva*

DATE
                                          G218   NG298   P300

LOCALITY

HABITAT

NOTES

Barn Swallow   *Hirundo rustica*

DATE
                                          G218   NG298   P202

LOCALITY

HABITAT

NOTES

Common House-Martin   *Delichon urbica*

DATE
                                          G–   NG–   P–

LOCALITY

HABITAT

NOTES

Jays, Magpies and Crows *(Corvidae)*

Gray Jay   *Perisoreus canadensis*

DATE
                                          G224   NG302   P208

LOCALITY

HABITAT

NOTES

Steller's Jay
Cyanocitta stelleri

DATE
                                         G222   NG302   P—

LOCALITY

HABITAT

NOTES

Blue Jay
Cyanocitta cristata

DATE
                                         G222   NG302   P208

LOCALITY

HABITAT

NOTES

Green Jay
Cyanocorax yncas

DATE
                                         G224   NG304   P—

LOCALITY

HABITAT

NOTES

Brown Jay
Cyanocorax morio

DATE
                                         G224   NG304   P—

LOCALITY

HABITAT

NOTES

G = Golden   **NG** = National Geographic   **P** = Peterson

Scrub Jay   *Aphelocoma coerulescens*

DATE
                                        G222   NG300   P208

LOCALITY

HABITAT

NOTES

Gray-breasted Jay   *Aphelocoma ultramarina*

DATE
                                        G222   NG300   P—

LOCALITY

HABITAT

NOTES

Pinyon Jay   *Gymnorhinus cyanocephalus*

DATE
                                        G222   NG300   P—

LOCALITY

HABITAT

NOTES

Clark's Nutcracker   *Nucifraga columbiana*

DATE
                                        G224   NG302   P—

LOCALITY

HABITAT

NOTES

G = Golden   NG = National Geographic   P = Peterson

Black-billed Magpie   *Pica pica*

DATE
                            G224   NG304   P208

LOCALITY

HABITAT

NOTES

Yellow-billed Magpie   *Pica nuttalli*

DATE
                            G224   NG304   P—

LOCALITY

HABITAT

NOTES

American Crow   *Corvus brachyrhynchos*

DATE
                            G226   NG306   P206

LOCALITY

HABITAT

NOTES

Northwestern Crow   *Corvus caurinus*

DATE
                            G226   NG306   P—

LOCALITY

HABITAT

NOTES

G = Golden   **NG** = National Geographic   **P** = Peterson

Mexican Crow   *Corvus imparatus*

DATE
                                                    G226   NG306   P—

LOCALITY

HABITAT

NOTES

Fish Crow   *Corvus ossifragus*

DATE
                                                    G226   NG306   P206

LOCALITY

HABITAT

NOTES

Chihuahuan Raven   *Corvus cryptoleucus*

DATE
                                                    G226   NG306   P206

LOCALITY

HABITAT

NOTES

Common Raven   *Corvus corax*

DATE
                                                    G226   NG306   P206

LOCALITY

HABITAT

NOTES

G = Golden   **NG** = National Geographic   **P** = Peterson

Black-capped Chickadee　　　　　*Parus atricapillus*　**Titmice *(Paridae)***

DATE
　　　　　　　　　　　　　　　　　G228　　NG310　　P210

LOCALITY

HABITAT

NOTES

Carolina Chickadee　　　　　　　　*Parus carolinensis*

DATE
　　　　　　　　　　　　　　　　　G228　　NG310　　P210

LOCALITY

HABITAT

NOTES

Mexican Chickadee　　　　　　　　　*Parus sclateri*

DATE
　　　　　　　　　　　　　　　　　G228　　NG310　　P—

LOCALITY

HABITAT

NOTES

Mountain Chickadee　　　　　　　　*Parus gambeli*

DATE
　　　　　　　　　　　　　　　　　G228　　NG310　　P—

LOCALITY

HABITAT

NOTES

Siberian Tit   *Parus cinctus*
DATE
                                          G228   NG312   P—
LOCALITY

HABITAT

NOTES

Boreal Chickadee   *Parus hudsonicus*
DATE
                                          G228   NG312   P210
LOCALITY

HABITAT

NOTES

Chestnut-backed Chickadee   *Parus rufescens*
DATE
                                          G228   NG312   P—
LOCALITY

HABITAT

NOTES

Bridled Titmouse   *Parus wollweberi*
DATE
                                          G230   NG308   P—
LOCALITY

HABITAT

NOTES

G = Golden   NG = National Geographic   P = Peterson

Plain Titmouse   *Parus inornatus*
DATE
G230   NG308   P—
LOCALITY

HABITAT

NOTES

Tufted Titmouse   *Parus bicolor*
DATE
G230   NG308   P210
LOCALITY

HABITAT

NOTES

Verdin   *Auriparus flaviceps*   **Verdins**
DATE
G232   NG312   P—   *(Remizidae)*
LOCALITY

HABITAT

NOTES

Bushtit   *Psaltriparus minimus*   **Bushtits**
DATE
G232   NG312   P—   *(Aegithalidae)*
LOCALITY

HABITAT

NOTES

Nuthatches
(*Sittidae*)

Red-breasted Nuthatch   *Sitta canadensis*

DATE   G234   NG314   P212

LOCALITY

HABITAT

NOTES

White-breasted Nuthatch   *Sitta carolinensis*

DATE   G234   NG314   P212

LOCALITY

HABITAT

NOTES

Pygmy Nuthatch   *Sitta pygmaea*

DATE   G234   NG314   P—

LOCALITY

HABITAT

NOTES

Brown-headed Nuthatch   *Sitta pusilla*

DATE   G234   NG314   P212

LOCALITY

HABITAT

NOTES

G = Golden   NG = National Geographic   P = Peterson

Brown Creeper
Certhia americana

Creepers
(Certhiidae)

G234   NG314   P212

DATE _____

LOCALITY _____

HABITAT _____

NOTES _____

_____

Red-whiskered Bulbul
Pycnonotus jocosus

Bulbuls
(Pycnonotidae)

G232   NG346   P216

DATE _____

LOCALITY _____

HABITAT _____

NOTES _____

_____

Cactus Wren
Campylorhynchus brunneicapillus

Wrens
(Troglodytidae)

G238   NG318   P—

DATE _____

LOCALITY _____

HABITAT _____

NOTES _____

_____

Rock Wren
Salpinctes obsoletus

G238   NG318   P214

DATE _____

LOCALITY _____

HABITAT _____

NOTES _____

_____

G = Golden   NG = National Geographic   P = Peterson

Canyon Wren   *Catherpes mexicanus*

DATE   G238   NG318   P—

LOCALITY

HABITAT

NOTES

Carolina Wren   *Thryothorus ludovicianus*

DATE   G236   NG316   P214

LOCALITY

HABITAT

NOTES

Bewick's Wren   *Thryomanes bewickii*

DATE   G236   NG316   P214

LOCALITY

HABITAT

NOTES

House Wren   *Troglodytes aedon*

DATE   G236   NG316   P214

LOCALITY

HABITAT

NOTES

G = Golden   NG = National Geographic   P = Peterson

Winter Wren
Troglodytes troglodytes

DATE

G236   NG316   P214

LOCALITY

HABITAT

NOTES

Sedge Wren
Cistothorus platensis

DATE

G238   NG318   P214

LOCALITY

HABITAT

NOTES

Marsh Wren
Cistothorus palustris

DATE

G238   NG318   P214

LOCALITY

HABITAT

NOTES

American Dipper
Cinclus mexicanus

DATE

G232   NG342   P—

LOCALITY

HABITAT

NOTES

Dippers
(Muscicapidae)

G = Golden   NG = National Geographic   P = Peterson

Old World Warblers, Kinglets and Gnatcatchers; Old World Flycatchers and Allies; Solitaires, Thrushes and Allies (Muscicapidae)

Middendorf's Grasshopper Warbler — *Locustella ochotensis*

DATE   G—   NG320   P—

LOCALITY

HABITAT

NOTES

Wood Warbler — *Phylloscopus sibilatrix*

DATE   G—   NG—   P—

LOCALITY

HABITAT

NOTES

Dusky Warbler — *Phylloscopus fuscatus*

DATE   G—   NG320   P—

LOCALITY

HABITAT

NOTES

Arctic Warbler — *Phylloscopus borealis*

DATE   G254   NG320   P—

LOCALITY

HABITAT

NOTES

Golden-crowned Kinglet   *Regulus satrapa*

DATE ·

| | | | G252 | NG322 | P216 |

LOCALITY

HABITAT

NOTES

Ruby-crowned Kinglet   *Regulus calendula*

DATE

| | | | G252 | NG322 | P216 |

LOCALITY

HABITAT

NOTES

Blue-gray Gnatcatcher   *Polioptila caerulea*

DATE

| | | | G252 | NG322 | P216 |

LOCALITY

HABITAT

NOTES

Black-tailed Gnatcatcher   *Polioptila melanura*

DATE

| | | | G252 | NG322 | P— |

LOCALITY

HABITAT

NOTES

Black-capped Gnatcatcher   *Polioptila nigriceps*

DATE   G252   NG322   P—

LOCALITY

HABITAT

NOTES

Red-breasted Flycatcher   *Ficedula parva*

DATE   G—   NG320   P—

LOCALITY

HABITAT

NOTES

Siberian Flycatcher   *Muscicapa sibirica*

DATE   G—   NG—   P—

LOCALITY

HABITAT

NOTES

Gray-spotted Flycatcher   *Muscicapa griseisticta*

DATE   G254   NG320   P—

LOCALITY

HABITAT

NOTES

Siberian Rubythroat   *Luscinia calliope*

DATE
                                              G246   NG332   P—

LOCALITY

HABITAT

NOTES

Bluethroat   *Luscinia svecica*

DATE
                                              G246   NG332   P—

LOCALITY

HABITAT

NOTES

Northern Wheatear   *Oenanthe oenanthe*

DATE
                                              G246   NG332   P220

LOCALITY

HABITAT

NOTES

Eastern Bluebird   *Sialia sialis*

DATE
                                              G250   NG324   P220

LOCALITY

HABITAT

NOTES

Western Bluebird   *Sialia mexicana*

DATE   **G**250   **NG**324   **P**—

LOCALITY

HABITAT

NOTES

Mountain Bluebird   *Sialia currucoides*

DATE   **G**250   **NG**324   **P**220

LOCALITY

HABITAT

NOTES

Townsend's Solitaire   *Myadestes townsendi*

DATE   **G**246   **NG**324   **P**218

LOCALITY

HABITAT

NOTES

Veery   *Catharus fuscescens*

DATE   **G**248   **NG**326   **P**222

LOCALITY

HABITAT

NOTES

G = Golden   **NG** = National Geographic   **P** = Peterson

Gray-cheeked Thrush   *Catharus minimus*

DATE
                G248   NG326   P222

LOCALITY

HABITAT

NOTES

Swainson's Thrush   *Catharus ustulatus*

DATE
                G248   NG326   P222

LOCALITY

HABITAT

NOTES

Hermit Thrush   *Catharus guttatus*

DATE
                G248   NG326   P222

LOCALITY

HABITAT

NOTES

Wood Thrush   *Hylocichla mustelina*

DATE
                G248   NG326   P222

LOCALITY

HABITAT

NOTES

G = Golden   NG = National Geographic   P = Peterson

Eye-browed Thrush   *Turdus obscurus*

DATE
                                                    G246   NG328   P—

LOCALITY

HABITAT

NOTES

Dusky Thrush   *Turdus naumanni*

DATE
                                                    G246   NG328   P—

LOCALITY

HABITAT

NOTES

Fieldfare   *Turdus pilaris*

DATE
                                                    G244   NG328   P296

LOCALITY

HABITAT

NOTES

Clay-colored Robin   *Turdus grayi*

DATE
                                                    G244   NG330   P—

LOCALITY

HABITAT

NOTES

G = Golden   NG = National Geographic   P = Peterson

Rufous-backed Robin   *Turdus rufopalliatus*

DATE   G244   NG330   P—

LOCALITY

HABITAT

NOTES

American Robin   *Turdus migratorius*

DATE   G244   NG330   P220

LOCALITY

HABITAT

NOTES

Varied Thrush   *Ixoreus naevius*

DATE   G246   NG328   P220

LOCALITY

HABITAT

NOTES

Aztec Thrush   *Ridgwayia pinicola*

DATE   G—   NG330   P—

LOCALITY

HABITAT

NOTES

Wrentit *Chamaea fasciata*

DATE

           G232 NG308 P—

LOCALITY

HABITAT

NOTES

Mockingbirds, Thrashers and Allies *(Mimidae)*

Gray Catbird *Dumetella carolinensis*

DATE

           G240 NG334 P218

LOCALITY

HABITAT

NOTES

Northern Mockingbird *Mimus polyglottos*

DATE

           G240 NG336 P218

LOCALITY

HABITAT

NOTES

Bahama Mockingbird *Mimus gundlachii*

DATE

           G— NG336 P300

LOCALITY

HABITAT

NOTES

Sage Thrasher   *Oreoscoptes montanus*
DATE
                                                     G240   **NG**336   **P**—

LOCALITY

HABITAT

NOTES

Brown Thrasher   *Toxostoma rufum*
DATE
                                                     G240   **NG**336   **P**218

LOCALITY

HABITAT

NOTES

Long-billed Thrasher   *Toxostoma longirostre*
DATE
                                                   G240   **NG**336   **P**—

LOCALITY

HABITAT

NOTES

Bendire's Thrasher   *Toxostoma bendirei*
DATE
                                                   G242   **NG**338   **P**—

LOCALITY

HABITAT

NOTES

Curve-billed Thrasher   *Toxostoma curvirostre*

DATE
                                             G242   NG338   P—

LOCALITY

HABITAT

NOTES

California Thrasher   *Toxostoma redivivum*

DATE
                                             G242   NG338   P—

LOCALITY

HABITAT

NOTES

Crissal Thrasher   *Toxostoma dorsale*

DATE
                                             G242   NG338   P—

LOCALITY

HABITAT

NOTES

Le Conte's Thrasher   *Toxostoma lecontei*

DATE
                                             G242   NG338   P—

LOCALITY

HABITAT

NOTES

G = Golden   **NG** = National Geographic   **P** = Peterson

Siberian Accentor

Prunella montanella

Accentors *(Prunellidae)*

G— NG332 P—

DATE

LOCALITY

HABITAT

NOTES

Yellow Wagtail

Motacilla flava

Wagtails and Pipits *(Motacillidae)*

G254 NG342 P—

DATE

LOCALITY

HABITAT

NOTES

Gray Wagtail

Motacilla cinerea

G254 NG342 P—

DATE

LOCALITY

HABITAT

NOTES

White Wagtail

Motacilla alba

G254 NG342 P—

DATE

LOCALITY

HABITAT

NOTES

Black-backed Wagtail
Motacilla lugens

DATE
G254   NG342   P—

LOCALITY

HABITAT

NOTES

Brown Tree-Pipit
Anthus trivialis

DATE
G256   NG—   P—

LOCALITY

HABITAT

NOTES

Olive Tree-Pipit
Anthus hodgsoni

DATE
G256   NG340   P—

LOCALITY

HABITAT

NOTES

Pechora Pipit
Anthus gustavi

DATE
G256   NG340   P—

LOCALITY

HABITAT

NOTES

G = Golden   **NG** = National Geographic   **P** = Peterson

Red-throated Pipit
Anthus cervinus

DATE

G256   NG340   P—

LOCALITY

HABITAT

NOTES

Water Pipit
Anthus spinoletta

DATE

G256   NG340   P200

LOCALITY

HABITAT

NOTES

Sprague's Pipit
Anthus spragueii

DATE

G256   NG340   P200

LOCALITY

HABITAT

NOTES

Bohemian Waxwing
Bombycilla garrulus

DATE

G258   NG344   P224

LOCALITY

HABITAT

NOTES

Waxwings
(Bombycillidae)

Cedar Waxwing   *Bombycilla cedrorum*

DATE
                                                 G258   **NG**344   **P**224

LOCALITY

HABITAT

NOTES

Silky Flycatchers (*Ptilogonatidae*)

Phainopepla   *Phainopepla nitens*

DATE
                                                 G258   **NG**344   **P**–

LOCALITY

HABITAT

NOTES

Shrikes (*Laniidae*)

Brown Shrike   *Lanius cristatus*

DATE
                                                 G–   **NG**–   **P**–

LOCALITY

HABITAT

NOTES

Northern Shrike   *Lanius excubitor*

DATE
                                                 G260   **NG**334   **P**224

LOCALITY

HABITAT

NOTES

G = Golden   **NG** = National Geographic   **P** = Peterson

Loggerhead Shrike
Lanius ludovicianus

DATE

G260   NG334   P224

LOCALITY

HABITAT

NOTES

European Starling
Sturnus vulgaris

DATE

G260   NG346   P256

LOCALITY

HABITAT

NOTES

Starlings and Allies *(Sturnidae)*

Crested Myna
Acridotheres cristatellus

DATE

G260   NG346   P—

LOCALITY

HABITAT

NOTES

White-eyed Vireo
Vireo griseus

DATE

G264   NG348   P228

LOCALITY

HABITAT

NOTES

Vireos *(Vireonidae)*

Bell's Vireo
Vireo bellii

DATE

G264   NG350   P228

LOCALITY

HABITAT

NOTES

Black-capped Vireo
Vireo atricapillus

DATE

G262   NG348   P228

LOCALITY

HABITAT

NOTES

Gray Vireo
Vireo vicinior

DATE

G262   NG350   P—

LOCALITY

HABITAT

NOTES

Solitary Vireo
Vireo solitarius

DATE

G262   NG350   P228

LOCALITY

HABITAT

NOTES

Yellow-throated Vireo   *Vireo flavifrons*

DATE
                                    G264   NG348   P228

LOCALITY

HABITAT

NOTES

Hutton's Vireo   *Vireo huttoni*

DATE
                                    G264   NG350   P—

LOCALITY

HABITAT

NOTES

Warbling Vireo   *Vireo gilvus*

DATE
                                    G266   NG352   P226

LOCALITY

HABITAT

NOTES

Philadelphia Vireo   *Vireo philadelphicus*

DATE
                                    G266   NG352   P226

LOCALITY

HABITAT

NOTES

Red-eyed Vireo   *Vireo olivaceus*

DATE
                                          G266   NG352   P226

LOCALITY

HABITAT

NOTES

___

Black-whiskered Vireo   *Vireo altiloquus*

DATE
                                          G266   NG352   P226

LOCALITY

HABITAT

NOTES

___

**Wood Warblers;
Bananaquits;
Tanagers;
Cardinals &
Grosbeaks;
Sparrows;
Blackbirds; and
Allies
(Emberizidae)**

Bachman's Warbler   *Vermivora bachmanii*

DATE
                                          G272   NG356   P242

LOCALITY

HABITAT

NOTES

___

Blue-winged Warbler   *Vermivora pinus*

DATE
                                          G272   NG354   P238

LOCALITY

HABITAT

NOTES

___

Golden-winged Warbler   *Vermivora chrysoptera*

DATE

                 G272   **NG**354   **P**242

LOCALITY

HABITAT

NOTES

Tennessee Warbler   *Vermivora peregrina*

DATE

                 G274   **NG**356   **P**240

LOCALITY

HABITAT

NOTES

Orange-crowned Warbler   *Vermivora celata*

DATE

                 G274   **NG**356   **P**240

LOCALITY

HABITAT

NOTES

Nashville Warbler   *Vermivora ruficapilla*

DATE

                 G274   **NG**358   **P**244

LOCALITY

HABITAT

NOTES

Virginia's Warbler   *Vermivora virginiae*

DATE

G276   NG358   P—

LOCALITY

HABITAT

NOTES

Colima Warbler   *Vermivora crissalis*

DATE

G276   NG358   P—

LOCALITY

HABITAT

NOTES

Lucy's Warbler   *Vermivora luciae*

DATE

G276   NG358   P—

LOCALITY

HABITAT

NOTES

Northern Parula   *Parula americana*

DATE

G276   NG358   P230

LOCALITY

HABITAT

NOTES

G = Golden   NG = National Geographic   P = Peterson

Tropical Parula   *Parula pitiayumi*

DATE
                               G276   NG358   P—

LOCALITY

HABITAT

NOTES

Crescent-chested Warbler   *Vermivora superciliosa*

DATE
                               G—   NG—   P—

LOCALITY

HABITAT

NOTES

Yellow Warbler   *Dendroica petechia*

DATE
                               G278   NG370   P238

LOCALITY

HABITAT

NOTES

Chestnut-sided Warbler   *Dendroica pensylvanica*

DATE
                               G284   NG362   P236

LOCALITY

HABITAT

NOTES

G = Golden   NG = National Geographic   P = Peterson

Magnolia Warbler   *Dendroica magnolia*

DATE   G278   NG362   P234

LOCALITY

HABITAT

NOTES

Cape May Warbler   *Dendroica tigrina*

DATE   G278   NG362   P236

LOCALITY

HABITAT

NOTES

Black-throated Blue Warbler   *Dendroica caerulescens*

DATE   G282   NG360   P232

LOCALITY

HABITAT

NOTES

Yellow-rumped Warbler   *Dendroica coronata*

DATE   G278   NG362   P234

LOCALITY

HABITAT

NOTES

Black-throated Gray Warbler *Dendroica nigrescens*

DATE
G282   NG364   P232

LOCALITY

HABITAT

NOTES

Townsend's Warbler *Dendroica townsendi*

DATE
G280   NG364   P—

LOCALITY

HABITAT

NOTES

Hermit Warbler *Dendroica occidentalis*

DATE
G280   NG364   P—

LOCALITY

HABITAT

NOTES

Black-throated Green Warbler *Dendroica virens*

DATE
G280   NG364   P230

LOCALITY

HABITAT

NOTES

Golden-cheeked Warbler   *Dendroica chrysoparia*

DATE   G280   NG364   P—

LOCALITY

HABITAT

NOTES

Blackburnian Warbler   *Dendroica fusca*

DATE   G284   NG360   P236

LOCALITY

HABITAT

NOTES

Yellow-throated Warbler   *Dendroica dominica*

DATE   G282   NG366   P230

LOCALITY

HABITAT

NOTES

Grace's Warbler   *Dendroica graciae*

DATE   G282   NG366   P—

LOCALITY

HABITAT

NOTES

Pine Warbler   *Dendroica pinus*

DATE

| | G286 | NG368 | P238 |

LOCALITY

HABITAT

NOTES

Kirtland's Warbler   *Dendroica kirtlandii*

DATE

| | G286 | NG366 | P234 |

LOCALITY

HABITAT

NOTES

Prairie Warbler   *Dendroica discolor*

DATE

| | G286 | NG366 | P238 |

LOCALITY

HABITAT

NOTES

Palm Warbler   *Dendroica palmarum*

DATE

| | G286 | NG368 | P238 |

LOCALITY

HABITAT

NOTES

Bay-breasted Warbler   *Dendroica castanea*

DATE   G284   NG368   P236

LOCALITY

HABITAT

NOTES

Blackpoll Warbler   *Dendroica striata*

DATE   G284   NG368   P232

LOCALITY

HABITAT

NOTES

Cerulean Warbler   *Dendroica cerulea*

DATE   G282   NG360   P232

LOCALITY

HABITAT

NOTES

Black-and-white Warbler   *Mniotilta varia*

DATE   G270   NG360   P232

LOCALITY

HABITAT

NOTES

American Redstart *Setophaga ruticilla*

DATE

G292   NG378   P236

LOCALITY

HABITAT

NOTES

Prothonotary Warbler *Protonotaria citrea*

DATE

G270   NG354   P230

LOCALITY

HABITAT

NOTES

Worm-eating Warbler *Helmitheros vermivorus*

DATE

G270   NG374   P240

LOCALITY

HABITAT

NOTES

Swainson's Warbler *Limnothlypis swainsonii*

DATE

G270   NG374   P240

LOCALITY

HABITAT

NOTES

G = Golden   **NG** = National Geographic   **P** = Peterson

Ovenbird   *Seiurus aurocapillus*

DATE
                                        G288   NG374   P246

LOCALITY

HABITAT

NOTES

Northern Waterthrush   *Seiurus noveboracensis*

DATE
                                        G288   NG374   P246

LOCALITY

HABITAT

NOTES

Louisiana Waterthrush   *Seiurus motacilla*

DATE
                                        G288   NG374   P246

LOCALITY

HABITAT

NOTES

Kentucky Warbler   *Oporornis formosus*

DATE
                                        G290   NG372   P244

LOCALITY

HABITAT

NOTES

Connecticut Warbler   *Oporornis agilis*

DATE
                                    G290   NG370   P244

LOCALITY

HABITAT

NOTES

Mourning Warbler   *Oporornis philadelphia*

DATE
                                    G290   NG370   P244

LOCALITY

HABITAT

NOTES

MacGillivray's Warbler   *Oporornis tolmiei*

DATE
                                    G290   NG370   P—

LOCALITY

HABITAT

NOTES

Common Yellowthroat   *Geothlypis trichas*

DATE
                                    G288   NG376   P246

LOCALITY

HABITAT

NOTES

G = Golden   NG = National Geographic   P = Peterson

Gray-crowned Yellowthroat | *Geothlypis poliocephala*

DATE   G288   NG—   P—

LOCALITY

HABITAT

NOTES

Hooded Warbler | *Wilsonia citrina*

DATE   G292   NG372   P242

LOCALITY

HABITAT

NOTES

Wilson's Warbler | *Wilsonia pusilla*

DATE   G292   NG372   P242

LOCALITY

HABITAT

NOTES

Canada Warbler | *Wilsonia canadensis*

DATE   G292   NG372   P234

LOCALITY

HABITAT

NOTES

G = Golden   NG = National Geographic   P = Peterson

Red-faced Warbler

Cardellina rubrifrons

DATE

G292   NG378   P—

LOCALITY

HABITAT

NOTES

Painted Redstart

Myioborus pictus

DATE

G292   NG378   P—

LOCALITY

HABITAT

NOTES

Slate-throated Redstart

Myioborus miniatus

DATE

G—   NG378   P—

LOCALITY

HABITAT

NOTES

Fan-tailed Warbler

Euthlypis lachrymosa

DATE

G—   NG—   P—

LOCALITY

HABITAT

NOTES

G = Golden   NG = National Geographic   P = Peterson

Golden-crowned Warbler   *Basileuterus culicivorus*

DATE   G—   NG376   P—

LOCALITY

HABITAT

NOTES

Rufous-capped Warbler   *Basileuterus rufifrons*

DATE   G—   NG376   P—

LOCALITY

HABITAT

NOTES

Yellow-breasted Chat   *Icteria virens*

DATE   G288   NG376   P246

LOCALITY

HABITAT

NOTES

Olive Warbler   *Peucedramus taeniatus*

DATE   G274   NG378   P—

LOCALITY

HABITAT

NOTES

Bananaquit   *Coereba flaveola*

DATE
                                          G262   NG432   P300
LOCALITY

HABITAT

NOTES

Stripe-headed Tanager   *Spindalis zena*

DATE
                                          G306   NG432   P300
LOCALITY

HABITAT

NOTES

Hepatic Tanager   *Piranga flava*

DATE
                                          G306   NG430   P—
LOCALITY

HABITAT

NOTES

Summer Tanager   *Piranga rubra*

DATE
                                          G306   NG430   P260
LOCALITY

HABITAT

NOTES

Scarlet Tanager   *Piranga olivacea*

DATE

G306   NG430   P260

LOCALITY

HABITAT

NOTES

Western Tanager   *Piranga ludoviciana*

DATE

G306   NG430   P260

LOCALITY

HABITAT

NOTES

Crimson-collared Grosbeak   *Rhodothraupus celaeno*

DATE

G—   NG—   P—

LOCALITY

HABITAT

NOTES

Northern Cardinal   *Cardinalis cardinalis*

DATE

G308   NG382   P268

LOCALITY

HABITAT

NOTES

G = Golden   **NG** = National Geographic   **P** = Peterson

Pyrrhuloxia   *Cardinalis sinuatus*

DATE

G308   **NG**382   **P**—

LOCALITY

HABITAT

NOTES

Yellow Grosbeak   *Pheucticus chrysopeplus*

DATE

G—   **NG**380   **P**—

LOCALITY

HABITAT

NOTES

Rose-breasted Grosbeak   *Pheucticus ludovicianus*

DATE

G310   **NG**380   **P**276

LOCALITY

HABITAT

NOTES

Black-headed Grosbeak   *Pheucticus melanocephalus*

DATE

G310   **NG**380   **P**276

LOCALITY

HABITAT

NOTES

Blue Bunting   *Cyanocompsa parellina*

DATE   G—   NG382   P—

LOCALITY

HABITAT

NOTES

Blue Grosbeak   *Guiraca caerulea*

DATE   G310   NG382   P274

LOCALITY

HABITAT

NOTES

Lazuli Bunting   *Passerina amoena*

DATE   G312   NG384   P274

LOCALITY

HABITAT

NOTES

Indigo Bunting   *Passerina cyanea*

DATE   G312   NG384   P274

LOCALITY

HABITAT

NOTES

Varied Bunting   *Passerina versicolor*

DATE
                                                    G312   NG384   P—

LOCALITY

HABITAT

NOTES

Painted Bunting   *Passerina ciris*

DATE
                                                    G312   NG384   P274

LOCALITY

HABITAT

NOTES

Dickcissel   *Spiza americana*

DATE
                                                    G322   NG416   P262

LOCALITY

HABITAT

NOTES

Olive Sparrow   *Arremonops rufivirgatus*

DATE
                                                    G324   NG386   P—

LOCALITY

HABITAT

NOTES

Green-tailed Towhee   *Pipilo chlorurus*

DATE
                                      G324   **NG**386   **P**276

LOCALITY

HABITAT

NOTES

Rufous-sided Towhee   *Pipilo erythrophthalmus*

DATE
    G324   **NG**386   **P**276

LOCALITY

HABITAT

NOTES

Brown Towhee   *Pipilo fuscus*

DATE
    G324   **NG**386   **P**—

LOCALITY

HABITAT

NOTES

Abert's Towhee   *Pipilo aberti*

DATE
    G324   **NG**386   **P**—

LOCALITY

HABITAT

NOTES

White-collared Seedeater

Sporophila torqueola

DATE

G322   NG416   P—

LOCALITY

HABITAT

NOTES

Black-faced Grassquit

Tiaris bicolor

DATE

G314   NG416   P300

LOCALITY

HABITAT

NOTES

Bachman's Sparrow

Aimophila aestivalis

DATE

G336   NG396   P282

LOCALITY

HABITAT

NOTES

Botteri's Sparrow

Aimophila botterii

DATE

G336   NG396   P—

LOCALITY

HABITAT

NOTES

Cassin's Sparrow   *Aimophila cassinii*

DATE
                                                       G336   NG396   P—

LOCALITY

HABITAT

NOTES

Rufous-winged Sparrow   *Aimophila carpalis*

DATE
                                                       G336   NG398   P—

LOCALITY

HABITAT

NOTES

Rufous-crowned Sparrow   *Aimophila ruficeps*

DATE
                                                       G336   NG398   P280

LOCALITY

HABITAT

NOTES

American Tree Sparrow   *Spizella arborea*

DATE
                                                       G338   NG398   P280

LOCALITY

HABITAT

NOTES

G = Golden   NG = National Geographic   P = Peterson

Chipping Sparrow   *Spizella passerina*

DATE

                                          G338   NG400   P280

LOCALITY

HABITAT

NOTES

Clay-colored Sparrow   *Spizella pallida*

DATE

                                          G338   NG400   P282

LOCALITY

HABITAT

NOTES

Brewer's Sparrow   *Spizella breweri*

DATE

                                          G338   NG400   P—

LOCALITY

HABITAT

NOTES

Field Sparrow   *Spizella pusilla*

DATE

                                          G338   NG398   P280

LOCALITY

HABITAT

NOTES

Black-chinned Sparrow   *Spizella atrogularis*

DATE
                                    G338   NG402   P—

LOCALITY

HABITAT

NOTES

Vesper Sparrow   *Pooecetes gramineus*

DATE
                                    G332   NG392   P284

LOCALITY

HABITAT

NOTES

Lark Sparrow   *Chondestes grammacus*

DATE
                                    G332   NG394   P282

LOCALITY

HABITAT

NOTES

Black-throated Sparrow   *Amphispiza bilineata*

DATE
                                    G332   NG394   P—

LOCALITY

HABITAT

NOTES

Sage Sparrow   *Amphispiza belli*

DATE

           G332   NG394   P—

LOCALITY

HABITAT

NOTES

Five-striped Sparrow   *Amphispiza quinquestriata*

DATE

           G336   NG394   P—

LOCALITY

HABITAT

NOTES

Lark Bunting   *Calamospiza melanocorys*

DATE

           G332   NG416   P262

LOCALITY

HABITAT

NOTES

Savannah Sparrow   *Passerculus sandwichensis*

DATE

           G328   NG392   P286

LOCALITY

HABITAT

NOTES

G = Golden   **NG** = National Geographic   **P** = Peterson

Baird's Sparrow   *Ammodramus bairdii*

DATE

G328   NG388   P286

LOCALITY

HABITAT

NOTES

Grasshopper Sparrow   *Ammodramus savannarum*

DATE

G328   NG388   P282

LOCALITY

HABITAT

NOTES

Henslow's Sparrow   *Ammodramus henslowii*

DATE

G328   NG388   P286

LOCALITY

HABITAT

NOTES

Le Conte's Sparrow   *Ammodramus leconteii*

DATE

G330   NG390   P288

LOCALITY

HABITAT

NOTES

Sharp-tailed Sparrow   *Ammodramus caudacutus*

DATE
                                        G330   NG390   P288

LOCALITY

HABITAT

NOTES

Seaside Sparrow   *Ammodramus maritimus*

DATE
                                        G330   NG390   P288

LOCALITY

HABITAT

NOTES

Fox Sparrow   *Passerella iliaca*

DATE
                                        G342   NG406   P284

LOCALITY

HABITAT

NOTES

Song Sparrow   *Melospiza melodia*

DATE
                                        G342   NG392   P284

LOCALITY

HABITAT

NOTES

Lincoln's Sparrow — *Melospiza lincolnii*

DATE   G342   NG406   P284

LOCALITY

HABITAT

NOTES

Swamp Sparrow — *Melospiza georgiana*

DATE   G342   NG406   P280

LOCALITY

HABITAT

NOTES

White-throated Sparrow — *Zonotrichia albicollis*

DATE   G340   NG404   P278

LOCALITY

HABITAT

NOTES

Golden-crowned Sparrow — *Zonotrichia atricapilla*

DATE   G340   NG404   P278

LOCALITY

HABITAT

NOTES

White-crowned Sparrow   *Zonotrichia leucophrys*

DATE

G340   NG404   P278

LOCALITY

HABITAT

NOTES

Harris' Sparrow   *Zonotrichia querula*

DATE

G340   NG404   P278

LOCALITY

HABITAT

NOTES

Dark-eyed Junco   *Junco hyemalis*

DATE

G334   NG402   P266

LOCALITY

HABITAT

NOTES

Yellow-eyed Junco   *Junco phaeonotus*

DATE

G334   NG402   P—

LOCALITY

HABITAT

NOTES

G = Golden   NG = National Geographic   P = Peterson

McCown's Longspur   *Calcarius mccownii*

DATE

G344   NG408   P264

LOCALITY

HABITAT

NOTES

Lapland Longspur   *Calcarius lapponicus*

DATE

G344   NG410   P264

LOCALITY

HABITAT

NOTES

Smith's Longspur   *Calcarius pictus*

DATE

G344   NG410   P264

LOCALITY

HABITAT

NOTES

Chestnut-collared Longspur   *Calcarius ornatus*

DATE

G344   NG408   P264

LOCALITY

HABITAT

NOTES

Little Bunting   *Emberiza pusilla*

DATE
                                        G—   NG414   P—

LOCALITY

HABITAT

NOTES

Rustic Bunting   *Emberiza rustica*

DATE
                                        G—   NG412   P—

LOCALITY

HABITAT

NOTES

Gray Bunting   *Emberiza variabilis*

DATE
                                        G—   NG414   P—

LOCALITY

HABITAT

NOTES

Pallas' Reed-Bunting   *Emberiza pallasi*

DATE
                                        G—   NG414   P—

LOCALITY

HABITAT

NOTES

G = Golden   **NG** = National Geographic   **P** = Peterson

Common Reed-Bunting   *Emberiza schoeniclus*
DATE   G—   NG414   P—

LOCALITY

HABITAT

NOTES

Snow Bunting   *Plectrophenax nivalis*
DATE   G344   NG412   P266

LOCALITY

HABITAT

NOTES

McKay's Bunting   *Plectrophenax hyperboreus*
DATE   G344   NG412   P—

LOCALITY

HABITAT

NOTES

Bobolink   *Dolichonyx oryzivorus*
DATE   G296   NG418   P256

LOCALITY

HABITAT

NOTES

Red-winged Blackbird
Agelaius phoeniceus

DATE

G298   NG420   P252

LOCALITY

HABITAT

NOTES

Tricolored Blackbird
Agelaius tricolor

DATE

G298   NG420   P—

LOCALITY

HABITAT

NOTES

Tawny-shouldered Blackbird
Agelaius humeralis

DATE

G—   NG—   P300

LOCALITY

HABITAT

NOTES

Eastern Meadowlark
Sturnella magna

DATE

G296   NG418   P256

LOCALITY

HABITAT

NOTES

Western Meadowlark   *Sturnella neglecta*

DATE

G296   NG418   P256

LOCALITY

HABITAT

NOTES

Yellow-headed Blackbird   *Xanthocephalus xanthocephalus*

DATE

G298   NG420   P252

LOCALITY

HABITAT

NOTES

Rusty Blackbird   *Euphagus carolinus*

DATE

G298   NG422   P254

LOCALITY

HABITAT

NOTES

Brewer's Blackbird   *Euphagus cyanocephalus*

DATE

G298   NG422   P254

LOCALITY

HABITAT

NOTES

Great-tailed Grackle   *Quiscalus mexicanus*

DATE
                                    G300   NG424   P254

LOCALITY

HABITAT

NOTES

Boat-tailed Grackle   *Quiscalus major*

DATE
                                    G300   NG424   P254

LOCALITY

HABITAT

NOTES

Common Grackle   *Quiscalus quiscula*

DATE
                                    G300   NG424   P254

LOCALITY

HABITAT

NOTES

Bronzed Cowbird   *Molothrus aeneus*

DATE
                                    G300   NG422   P—

LOCALITY

HABITAT

NOTES

Brown-headed Cowbird   *Molothrus ater*

DATE
G300   NG422   P252

LOCALITY

HABITAT

NOTES

Black-vented Oriole   *Icterus wagleri*

DATE
G—   NG—   P—

LOCALITY

HABITAT

NOTES

Orchard Oriole   *Icterus spurius*

DATE
G302   NG426   P258

LOCALITY

HABITAT

NOTES

Hooded Oriole   *Icterus cucullatus*

DATE
G304   NG428   P—

LOCALITY

HABITAT

NOTES

G = Golden   **NG** = National Geographic   **P** = Peterson

Streak-backed Oriole   *Icterus pustulatus*

DATE

           G304   **NG**428   **P**—

LOCALITY

HABITAT

NOTES

Spot-breasted Oriole   *Icterus pectoralis*

DATE

           G304   **NG**428   **P**258

LOCALITY

HABITAT

NOTES

Altamira Oriole   *Icterus gularis*

DATE

           G304   **NG**428   **P**—

LOCALITY

HABITAT

NOTES

Audubon's Oriole   *Icterus graduacauda*

DATE

           G302   **NG**426   **P**—

LOCALITY

HABITAT

NOTES

Northern Oriole   *Icterus galbula*

DATE

G304   NG426   P258

LOCALITY

HABITAT

NOTES

Scott's Oriole   *Icterus parisorum*

DATE

G302   NG426   P—

LOCALITY

HABITAT

NOTES

Finches and Allies
(Fringillidae)

Common Chaffinch   *Fringilla coelebs*

DATE

G—   NG—   P296

LOCALITY

HABITAT

NOTES

Brambling   *Fringilla montifringilla*

DATE

G314   NG442   P296

LOCALITY

HABITAT

NOTES

Rosy Finch   *Leucosticte arctoa*

DATE   G318   NG438   P—

LOCALITY

HABITAT

NOTES

Pine Grosbeak   *Pinicola enucleator*

DATE   G316   NG436   P270

LOCALITY

HABITAT

NOTES

Common Rosefinch   *Carpodacus erythrinus*

DATE   G314   NG440   P—

LOCALITY

HABITAT

NOTES

Purple Finch   *Carpodacus purpureus*

DATE   G316   NG440   P270

LOCALITY

HABITAT

NOTES

Cassin's Finch   *Carpodacus cassinii*

DATE
                                            G316   NG440   P—

LOCALITY

HABITAT

NOTES

House Finch   *Carpodacus mexicanus*

DATE
                                            G316   NG440   P270

LOCALITY

HABITAT

NOTES

Red Crossbill   *Loxia curvirostra*

DATE
                                            G322   NG436   P268

LOCALITY

HABITAT

NOTES

White-winged Crossbill   *Loxia leucoptera*

DATE
                                            G322   NG436   P268

LOCALITY

HABITAT

NOTES

G = Golden   **NG** = National Geographic   **P** = Peterson

Common Redpoll   *Carduelis flammea*

DATE
                                               G318   **NG**438   **P**270

LOCALITY

HABITAT

NOTES

Hoary Redpoll   *Carduelis hornemanni*

DATE
                                               G318   **NG**438   **P**270

LOCALITY

HABITAT

NOTES

Pine Siskin   *Carduelis pinus*

DATE
                                               G320   **NG**434   **P**272

LOCALITY

HABITAT

NOTES

Lesser Goldfinch   *Carduelis psaltria*

DATE
                                               G320   **NG**434   **P**—

LOCALITY

HABITAT

NOTES

Lawrence's Goldfinch
Carduelis lawrencei

DATE
                                                G320   NG434   P—

LOCALITY

HABITAT

NOTES

American Goldfinch
Carduelis tristis

DATE
                                                G320   NG434   P272

LOCALITY

HABITAT

NOTES

Oriental Greenfinch
Carduelis sinica

DATE
                                                G314   NG442   P—

LOCALITY

HABITAT

NOTES

Eurasian Bullfinch
Pyrrhula pyrrhula

DATE
                                                G314   NG442   P—

LOCALITY

HABITAT

NOTES

G = Golden   **NG** = National Geographic   **P** = Peterson

Evening Grosbeak — *Coccothraustes vespertinus*

G310   NG442   P272

DATE

LOCALITY

HABITAT

NOTES

Hawfinch — *Coccothraustes coccothraustes*

G314   NG442   P—

DATE

LOCALITY

HABITAT

NOTES

House Sparrow — *Passer domesticus*

G296   NG432   P262

DATE

LOCALITY

HABITAT

NOTES

Eurasian Tree Sparrow — *Passer montanus*

G296   NG432   P262

DATE

LOCALITY

HABITAT

NOTES

Old World Sparrows (Passeridae)

BIBLIOGRAPHY

Alden, Peter, and John Gooders. *Finding Birds Around the World*. Boston: Houghton Mifflin Co., 1981.

Cronin, Edward W., Jr. *Getting Started in Bird Watching*. Boston: Houghton, Mifflin Co., 1986.

Dennis, John V. *A Complete Guide to Bird Feeding*. New York: Alfred A. Knopf, 1984.

Farrand, John, Jr., Editor. *Audubon Society Master Guide to Birding*. 3 Vols. New York: Alfred A. Knopf, Inc., 1983.

Geffen, Alice M. *A Birdwatcher's Guide to the Eastern United States*. New York: Barron's/Woodbury, 1978.

Godfrey, W. Earl. *The Birds of Canada*. Ottawa: National Museums of Canada, 1979.

Griscom, Ludlow, and Alexander Sprunt, Jr. *The Warblers of America*. Garden City, New York: Doubleday & Co., Inc., 1979.

Harrison, Colin. *A Field Guide to the Nests, Eggs and Nestlings of North American Birds*. Cleveland: Collins, 1978.

Harrison, George H. *Roger Tory Peterson's Dozen Birding Hot Spots*. New York: Simon & Schuster, Inc., 1976.

———. *The Backyard Bird Watcher*. New York: Simon & Schuster, Inc., 1979.

Harrison, Hal. H. *Wood Warblers' World*. New York: Simon & Schuster, Inc., 1984.

Harrison, Peter. *Seabirds—An Identification Guide*. Boston: Houghton Mifflin Co., 1983.

———. *A Field Guide to Seabirds of the World*. Lexington, Massachusetts: The Stephen Greene Press, 1987.

Hayman, Peter, John Marchant, and Tony Prater. *Shorebirds—An Identification Guide*. Boston: Houghton Mifflin Co., 1986.

Hickey, Joseph J. *A Guide to Bird Watching*. New York: Dover Publications, 1975.

Johnsgard, Paul A. *Waterfowl of North America*. Bloomington and London: Indiana University Press, 1975.

Kastner, Joseph. *A World of Watchers*. San Francisco: Sierra Club Books, 1986.

Kitching, Jessie. *Birdwatcher's Guide to Wildlife Sanctuaries*. New York: Arco Publishing Co., Inc., 1976.

Laycock, George. *The Birdwatcher's Bible*. Garden City, New York: Doubleday & Co., Inc., 1976.

Lentz, Joan Easton, and Judith Young. *Birdwatching—A Guide for Beginners*. Santa Barbara, California: Capra Press, 1985.

Lotz, Aileen R. *Birding Around the World.* New York: Dodd, Mead & Co., 1987.

McElroy, Thomas P. *The Habitat Guide to Birding.* New York: Alfred A. Knopf, 1974.

National Geographic Society. *Field Guide to the Birds of North America.* Washington, D.C., 1987.

Peterson, Roger Tory. *A Field Guide to the Birds of Texas — and Adjacent States.* Boston: Houghton Mifflin Co., 1963.

———. *A Field Guide to Western Birds.* Second Edition. Boston: Houghton Mifflin Co., 1969.

———. *A Field Guide to the Birds — East of the Rockies.* Fourth Edition. Boston: Houghton Mifflin Co., 1980.

Pettengill, Olin Sewall, Jr. *A Guide to Bird Finding — East of the Mississippi.* Second Edition. New York: Oxford University Press, 1977.

———. *A Guide to Bird Finding — West of the Mississippi.* Second Edition. New York: Oxford University Press, 1981.

Piatt, Jean. *Adventures in Birding — Confessions of a Lister.* New York: Alfred A. Knopf, 1973.

Robbins, Chandler S., Bertel Brunn and Herbert S. Zim. *Birds of North America — A Guide to Field Identification.* Revised Edition. New York: Golden Press, 1983.

Socha, Laura O'Biso. *A Bird Watcher's Handbook.* New York: Dodd, Mead & Co., 1987.

Stokes, Donald W., and Lillian Q. *A Guide to Bird Behavior.* 3 Vols. Boston and Toronto: Little, Brown & Co., 1979.

Terres, John K. *The Audubon Society Encyclopedia of North American Birds.* New York: Alfred A. Knopf, 1980.

Tyrrell, Robert A., and Esther Quesada. *Hummingbirds — Their Life and Behavior.* New York: Crown Publishers, Inc., 1985.

Zimmer, Kevin J. *The Western Bird Watcher.* Englewood Cliffs, New Jersey: Prentice-Hall, Inc., 1985.